# HEATH
# ALGEBRA 1
## AN INTEGRATED APPROACH
## LARSON, KANOLD, STIFF

# FORMAL ASSESSMENT

## Norman B. Patterson

## Evelyn A. Wedzikowski

International Standard Book Number: 0-395-87198-0

4 5 6 7 8 9 10  HWI  01 00 99

McDougal Littell
Evanston, Illinois • Boston • Dallas

## Mid-Chapter Tests

For each chapter in the Student Text, there are two Mid-Chapter Tests, Forms A and B, which are of average difficulty.

(In the Alternative Assessment booklet there are partner forms of the Mid-Chapter Tests which provide opportunities for cooperative learning.)

## Chapter Tests

There are three Chapter Tests for each chapter in the Student Text. Forms A and B are of average difficulty and Form C is more challenging.

## Cumulative Tests

Cumulative Tests are of average difficulty and should be used after every third chapter in the Student Text.

| Chapters | Test | Use After | Form A | Form B | Form C |
|---|---|---|---|---|---|
| | | | Page | Page | Page |
| 1 | Mid-Chapter Test | Lesson 1.4 | 1 | 2 | --- |
| | Chapter Test | | 3 | 6 | 9 |
| 2 | Mid-Chapter Test | Lesson 2.4 | 12 | 13 | --- |
| | Chapter Test | | 14 | 17 | 20 |
| 3 | Mid-Chapter Test | Lesson 3.4 | 23 | 24 | --- |
| | Chapter Test | | 25 | 28 | 31 |
| 1–3 | Cumulative Test | | 34 | --- | --- |
| 4 | Mid-Chapter Test | Lesson 4.4 | 42 | 43 | --- |
| | Chapter Test | | 44 | 47 | 50 |
| 5 | Mid-Chapter Test | Lesson 5.4 | 53 | 54 | --- |
| | Chapter Test | | 55 | 58 | 61 |
| 6 | Mid-Chapter Test | Lesson 6.3 | 64 | 65 | --- |
| | Chapter Test | | 66 | 69 | 72 |
| 1–6 | Cumulative Test | | 75 | --- | --- |
| 7 | Mid-Chapter Test | Lesson 7.4 | 83 | 84 | --- |
| | Chapter Test | | 85 | 88 | 91 |
| 8 | Mid-Chapter Test | Lesson 8.4 | 94 | 95 | --- |
| | Chapter Test | | 96 | 99 | 102 |
| 9 | Mid-Chapter Test | Lesson 9.4 | 105 | 106 | --- |
| | Chapter Test | | 107 | 110 | 113 |
| 7–9 | Cumulative Test | | 116 | --- | --- |
| 10 | Mid-Chapter Test | Lesson 10.4 | 124 | 125 | --- |
| | Chapter Test | | 126 | 129 | 132 |
| 11 | Mid-Chapter Test | Lesson 11.4 | 135 | 136 | --- |
| | Chapter Test | | 137 | 140 | 143 |
| 12 | Mid-Chapter Test | Lesson 12.4 | 146 | 147 | --- |
| | Chapter Test | | 148 | 152 | 156 |
| 7–12 | Cumulative Test | | 160 | --- | --- |
| 13 | Mid-Chapter Test | Lesson 13.4 | 168 | 169 | --- |
| | Chapter Test | | 170 | 173 | 176 |

To help students prepare for college entrance tests, we have provided strategies for taking the tests, instructions for using the new answer forms for student-generated responses, and practice questions.

## Organization of Practice Questions

The practice questions are correlated to the chapters in the Student Text so that they require only information that has already been taught. The questions are also organized by type so that they provide organized practice in the three kinds of standardized test items: multiple choice, quantitative comparison, and student-generated response.

**Form A**
for each chapter:
multiple choice questions

**Form B**
for odd-numbered chapters:
quantitative comparisons

**Form B**
for even-numbered chapters:
student-generated responses

**Strategies for Taking College Entrance Tests • Page 179**

**Instructions for Recording Student-Generated Responses • Page 181**

**Answer Form for Student-Generated Responses • Page 182**

## Practice for College Entrance Tests

**ALTERNATIVE ASSESSMENT** copymasters for *ALGEBRA 1* are also available from D.C. Heath. These include practical suggestions for alternative assessment activities, Chapter Projects, Math Logs, and Partner Quizzes.

Name _____

Date _____

1. What is the product of 13 and 4?

1. _____

2. Evaluate the expression $[18 \div (7 + 2)] + 3$.

2. _____

3. Evaluate the expression $47.3 + (123.2 \div 14.3)$. Round the result to one decimal place.

3. _____

4. Evaluate the expression $3x(y - 5)$ when $x = 7$ and $y = 9$.

4. _____

5. Write $\frac{3}{5}$ as a decimal.

5. _____

6. What is 15% of 240?

6. _____

7. **Geometry**   The area of a circle is $A = \pi r^2$, where $\pi \approx 3.14$ and $r$ is the radius. Find the area of a circle to two decimal places if $r = 2.50$.

7. _____

8. **Charge Account**   The monthly interest rate on the unpaid balance of a charge account is 1.5%. How much interest is charged on an unpaid balance of $125.40?

8. _____

9. Which is larger, $3^4$ or $4^3$?

9. _____

10. Evaluate $7.4 + x \div 3.2$ when $x = 4.8$.

10. _____

Name _____

Date _____

1. What is the product of 33 and 5?

   1. _____

2. Evaluate the expression $52 - [28 \div (7 - 3)]$.

   2. _____

3. Evaluate the expression $83.4 + (219.8 \div 12.4)$. Round the result to one decimal place.

   3. _____

4. Evaluate the expression $5x(15 - y)$ when $x = 6$ and $y = 9$.

   4. _____

5. Write $\frac{3}{5}$ as a percent.

   5. _____

6. What is 24% of 1500?

   6. _____

7. **Geometry**  The area of a circle is $A = \pi r^2$, where $\pi \approx 3.14$ and $r$ is the radius. Find the area of a circle to two decimal places if $r = 3.60$.

   7. _____

8. **Charge Account**  The monthly interest rate on the unpaid balance of a charge account is 1.4%. How much interest is charged on an unpaid balance of $140.60?

   8. _____

9. Which is larger, $3^5$ or $5^3$?

   9. _____

10. Evaluate $9.8 + x \div 1.7$ when $x = 10.2$.

   10. _____

  *Algebra 1*

**1.** Evaluate the expression $25 \div [(2)(7) - 4]$.

1. _____

**2.** What is the quotient of 28 and 7?

2. _____

**3.** Evaluate the expression to two decimal places.

$$[48.9 - (43.2 \div 7.4)] - 17.5$$

3. _____

**4. *Geometry*** Find the perimeter of the triangle shown.

4. _____

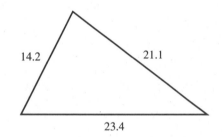

14.2    21.1

23.4

**5.** Write a variable expression for "the product of $x$ and 7, divided by 5."

5. _____

**6.** Evaluate $6y + (7 - 3y)$ when $y = 3$.

6. _____

**7. *Geometry*** A rectangle is twice as long as it is wide and its longer side is 14.2. Find its perimeter.

7. _____

**8.** Evaluate the expression $7.84x - 17.23$ to two decimal places when $x = 5.14$.

8. _____

**9.** *Geometry*  The circumference of a circle is $\pi$ times twice the radius where $\pi \approx 3.14$.  Find the circumference of a circle whose radius is 7.18 to two decimal places.

9. _____

**10.** *Geometry*  Write a variable expression for the volume of a cube whose side length is $x$.

10. _____

**11.** Evaluate the expression $x^3 + 3x - 5$ when $x = 2$.

11. _____

**12.** Evaluate $[(y - 2)^2 + 5] \div 3$ when $y = 4$.

12. _____

**13.** Is $x = 4$ a solution of the equation $2x - 4 = 8 + x$?

13. _____

**14.** Is $x = 7$ a solution of the inequality $5 + 2x \leq 15$?

14. _____

**15.** Write an algebraic expression for "three less than five times a number *x*."

15. _____

**16.** Write a verbal phrase for the algebraic expression $10 + \dfrac{x}{4}$.

16. _____

**17.** Write an equation or inequality for the verbal statement "seven is equal to 4 times a number *B*."

17. _____

**18.** Write an equation equivalent to the verbal statement "three times the sum of a number *n* and 7 is 16."

18. _____

**19.** *Awards Dinner*   An awards dinner costs $225 plus $5 for each person making reservations. The total bill is $735. How many people made reservations?

19. _____

**20.** *Company Employees*   The percentages of males and females working for a company in 1980 and 1990 are shown in the bar graph. What is the increase in the percentage of females employed for the ten year period?

20. _____

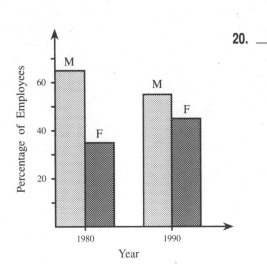

1. Evaluate the expression $36 \div [(3)(7) - 3]$.

   1. _____

2. What is the quotient of 35 and 7?

   2. _____

3. Evaluate the expression to two decimal places.

   $[(73.1 - 13.2) \div 3.8] - 2.06$

   3. _____

4. **Geometry**  Find the perimeter of the triangle shown.

   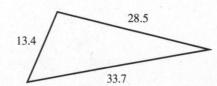

   4. _____

5. Write a variable expression for "the product of $x$ and 5, subtracted from 7."

   5. _____

6. Evaluate $8x + (5 - 5x)$ when $x = 5$.

   6. _____

7. **Geometry**  A rectangle is twice as long as it is wide and its longer side is 20.4. Find its perimeter.

   7. _____

**8.** Evaluate the expression $18.24x - 11.18$ to two decimal places when $x = 3.61$.

8. _____

**9.** *Geometry*   The circumference of a circle is $\pi$ times twice the radius where $\pi \approx 3.14$. Find the circumference of a circle whose radius is 9.43 to two decimal places.

9. _____

**10.** *Geometry*   Write a variable expression for the volume of a cube whose side length is $y$.

10. _____

**11.** Evaluate the expression $17 - x + 2x^3$ when $x = 2$.

11. _____

**12.** Evaluate $[(y + 3)^2 - 9] \div 8$ when $y = 4$.

12. _____

**13.** Is $x = 4$ a solution of the equation $2x + 4 = 8 + x$?

13. _____

**14.** Is $x = 2$ a solution of the inequality $5x - 2 \geq 7$?

14. _____

**15.** Write an algebraic expression for "five less than three times a number $x$."

15. _____

**16.** Write a verbal phrase for the algebraic expression $(10 + x) \div 4$.

16. _____

**17.** Write an equation or inequality for the verbal statement "seven is less than 4 times a number $B$."

17. _____

**18.** Write an equation equivalent to the verbal statement "the sum of three times a number $n$ and 7 is 16."

18. _____

**19.** *Awards Dinner*   An awards dinner costs $225 plus $5 for each person making reservations. The total bill is $1115. How many people made reservations?

19. _____

**20.** *Company Employees*   The percentages of males and females working for a company in 1980 and 1990 are shown in the bar graph. What is the decrease in the percentage of males employed for the ten-year period?

20. _____

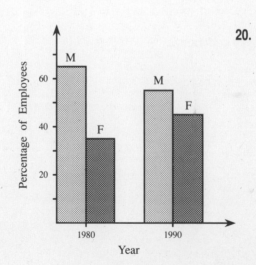

1. Evaluate the expression $\dfrac{48}{(3)(7)-5}$.

1. _____

2. Find the quotient of 24 and 9 to two decimal places.

2. _____

3. Evaluate the expression to two decimal places.

$$[(9.8 - 2.7) + (3.2)(7.1)] \div 14.5$$

3. _____

4. **Geometry**  Find the perimeter of the triangle shown.

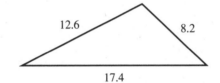

4. _____

5. Write a variable expression for "7 divided by the sum of $x$ and 5."

5. _____

6. Evaluate $3x - (14 - 2y)$ when $x = 3.5$ and $y = 10.5$.

6. _____

7. **Geometry**  A rectangle is twice as long as it is wide and its perimeter is 75. Find its dimensions.

7. _____

8. Evaluate the expression $\dfrac{18.91}{x + 2y}$ to two decimal places
when $x = 2.14$ and $y = 6.44$.

8. _____

9. **Geometry**  The area of a circle is $\pi$ times the square of the radius,
where $\pi \approx 3.14$. Find the area of a circle of radius 7.18 to two
decimal places.

9. _____

10. **Geometry**  Write a variable expression for the volume of a cube
whose side length is $A$.

10. _____

11. Evaluate the expression $16 + 12x - x^3$ when $x = 3$.

11. _____

12. Evaluate $(y + 3)^2 - 40 \div 8$ when $y = 4$.

12. _____

13. Is $x = 4$ a solution of the equation $2x + 1 = 8 + x \div 4$?

13. _____

14. Is $x = 2$ a solution of the inequality $7 + 3x \leq 7x - 2$?

14. _____

**15.** Write an algebraic expression for "three times the difference of a number *x* and 5."

15. _____

**16.** Write a verbal phrase for the algebraic expression $4 \div (10 + x)$.

16. _____

**17.** Write an equation or inequality for the verbal statement "seven is greater than or equal to 4 times a number *B*."

17. _____

**18.** Write an equation equivalent to the verbal statement "the sum of seven and three times a number *n* is 16."

18. _____

**19.** *Awards Dinner*   An awards dinner costs $275 plus $6 for each person making reservations. The total bill is $1547. How many people made reservations?

19. _____

**20.** *Company Employees*   The percentages of males and females working for a company in 1980 and 1990 are shown in the bar graph. Estimate the percentage of females the company employed in 1985.

20. _____

Name _____

Date _____

1. Graph the numbers on the number line: 3 and $-\frac{3}{2}$. Which is greater?

1. _____
   *Use graph at left.*

2. Write the numbers $-3, 4, -\frac{1}{2}, \frac{2}{3}, 0, 1$ in increasing order.

2. _____

3. Find the opposite of the number $-\frac{2}{3}$.

3. _____

4. Evaluate $|-3.7|$.

4. _____

5. Evaluate the expression $-5 + |-5| - |-3|$.

5. _____

6. Evaluate the expression $7.14 + (-3.25) - (7.12)$.

6. _____

7. Evaluate the expression $\left|-\frac{8}{5}\right| + \left|\frac{2}{5}\right| - \left|-\frac{3}{5}\right|$.

7. _____

8. Evaluate $-7 - (-5) + |x|$ when $x = -4$.

8. _____

9. Can the matrices, $\begin{bmatrix} 2 & 4 & 0 \\ -1 & 2 & 3 \end{bmatrix}$ and $\begin{bmatrix} 2 & 1 \\ -3 & 2 \\ -1 & 4 \end{bmatrix}$ be added?

9. _____

10. Find the sum of the matrices $\begin{bmatrix} 2 & -1 & 4 \\ 3 & 0 & -2 \end{bmatrix} + \begin{bmatrix} 7 & 0 & -3 \\ 1 & -2 & -1 \end{bmatrix}$.

10. _____

Name _____

Date _____

1. Graph the numbers on the number line: $-3$ and $\frac{3}{2}$. Which is greater?

    1. _____
    *Use graph at left.*

2. Write the numbers $-7, \frac{1}{2}, \frac{5}{4}, -3, 2, 0$ in increasing order.

    2. _____

3. Find the opposite of the number $\frac{7}{3}$.

    3. _____

4. Evaluate $|7.2|$.

    4. _____

5. Evaluate the expression $|-4| - 4 + |-2|$.

    5. _____

6. Evaluate the sum $-8.53 + 4.34 + (-1.15)$.

    6. _____

7. Evaluate the expression $\left|-\frac{7}{3}\right| + \left|\frac{8}{3}\right| - |-2|$.

    7. _____

8. Evaluate $-8 - (-5) - |-x|$ when $x = -4$.

    8. _____

9. Can the matrices, $\begin{bmatrix} 1 & -1 \\ 0 & -2 \\ 2 & 1 \end{bmatrix}$ and $\begin{bmatrix} 4 & -3 \\ 1 & -2 \\ 7 & -1 \end{bmatrix}$ be added?

    9. _____

10. Find the difference of the matrices $\begin{bmatrix} 2 & -1 & 4 \\ 3 & 0 & -2 \end{bmatrix} - \begin{bmatrix} 7 & 0 & -3 \\ 1 & -2 & -1 \end{bmatrix}$.

    10. _____

1. Write the numbers in *increasing* order.

   $\frac{3}{2}, -10, 0, \frac{2}{3}, -\frac{5}{4}, 1$

   1. _____

2. Graph the numbers, 1.5 and −2.5, on the number line. Which is greater?

   2. _____
   *Use graph at left.*

3. Find the opposite of the number $-\frac{6}{5}$.

   3. _____

4. Evaluate the expression $\left|-\frac{7}{3}\right|$.

   4. _____

5. Evaluate the sum $17.12 + (-5.23) + |1.72|$.

   5. _____

6. Simplify the expression $(-7) + 6 + [-(2 - 3)]$.

   6. _____

7. Evaluate the expression $28 - (-x) - |10|$ when $x = -15$.

   7. _____

8. Find the sum of the matrices $\begin{bmatrix} 2 & 0 \\ -1 & 4 \\ 3 & -2 \end{bmatrix} + \begin{bmatrix} -3 & 0 \\ -4 & 1 \\ 5 & -4 \end{bmatrix}$.

   8. _____

**9.** Find the difference of the matrices $\begin{bmatrix} 2 & 9 \\ 7 & 4 \end{bmatrix} - \begin{bmatrix} 8 & 3 \\ -2 & 1 \end{bmatrix}$.

9. _____

**10.** Find the product $8|-10|$.

10. _____

**11.** Find the product to 2 decimal places.

$$(-17.84)(1.52)(-3.20)$$

11. _____

**12.** *Shirt Purchase*    A man buys 5 shirts at \$13.75 each. Find his total bill.

12. _____

**13.** Evaluate the expression $3x^2 - 7x$ when $x = -3$.

13. _____

**14.** *Sales Commission*    A salesman gets a commission of \$2.75 on each item sold. One morning he sold 17 calculators and 12 pocket radios. Find his commission.

14. _____

**15.** Simplify the expression $3(2 - x) - 2(3 - x)$.

15. _____

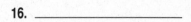
**16. *Buying Clothes***   You have $40.00. You wish to buy a T-shirt costing $14.50 and a pair of jeans costing $23.95. There is a 5% sales tax on clothing. Do you have enough money to pay for both?

16. _____

**17.** Remove parentheses by applying the Distributive Property.

$$20x(3 - 2x)$$

17. _____

**18.** Simplify the quotient $\dfrac{28x - 14}{7}$.

18. _____

**19.** Is $\dfrac{25 \text{ pounds}}{2.59 \text{ dollars}} \approx 9.65$ pounds per dollar a rate or a ratio?

19. _____

**20. *Gasoline Consumption***   A motorist travels 337 miles while using 13.7 gallons of gasoline. Find the gasoline consumption in miles per gallon to one decimal place.

20. _____

Ⓒ D. C. Heath and Company   *Algebra 1*

**1.** Write the numbers in *increasing* order.

$$7, -\frac{5}{6}, \frac{2}{3}, 0, -\frac{1}{2}, \frac{4}{5}$$

1. _____

**2.** Graph the numbers, $-1.5$ and $2.5$, on the number line. Which is greater?

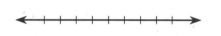

2. _____
*Use graph at left.*

**3.** Find the opposite of the number $\frac{6}{5}$.

3. _____

**4.** Evaluate the expression $-\left|\frac{7}{3}\right|$.

4. _____

**5.** Evaluate the sum $28.43 + (-13.17) + |2.07|$.

5. _____

**6.** Simplify the expression $-[-(4+3)]$.

6. _____

**7.** Evaluate the expression $35 - (-x) - |15|$ when $x = -5$.

7. _____

**8.** Find the sum of the matrices $\begin{bmatrix} 3 & -1 \\ 4 & 7 \\ -10 & 2 \end{bmatrix} + \begin{bmatrix} -5 & 4 \\ -3 & 2 \\ 1 & 0 \end{bmatrix}$.

8. _____

9. Find the difference of the matrices $\begin{bmatrix} 9 & -3 \\ 4 & 8 \end{bmatrix} - \begin{bmatrix} 2 & 7 \\ -8 & 4 \end{bmatrix}$.

9. _____

10. Find the product $(-8)|-10|$.

10. _____

11. Find the product to 2 decimal places.

$(9.83)(-7.24)(1.16)$

11. _____

12. **Shirt Purchase**    A man buys 7 shirts at $16.50 each. Find his total bill.

12. _____

13. Evaluate the expression $7x - 3x^2$ when $x = -2$.

13. _____

14. **Sales Commission**    A salesman gets a commission of $3.15 on each item sold. One morning he sold 12 calculators and 16 pocket radios. Find his commission.

14. _____

15. Simplify the expression $2(2 - x) - 3(3 - x)$.

15. _____

16. ***Buying Clothes***   You have $40.00.  You wish to buy a T-shirt
    costing $14.50 and a pair of jeans costing $23.95.  There is a 4%
    sales tax on clothing.  Do you have enough money to pay for both?

    16. _____

17. Remove parentheses by applying the Distributive Property.

    $17x(3x - 5)$

    17. _____

18. Simplify the quotient $\dfrac{30 - 18x}{6}$.

    18. _____

19. Is $\dfrac{15.75 \text{ dollars}}{2.30 \text{ pounds}} \approx \$6.85$ per pound a rate or a ratio?

    19. _____

20. ***Gasoline Consumption***   A motorist travels 523 miles while using
    16.2 gallons of gasoline.  Find the gasoline consumption in miles per
    gallon to one decimal place.

    20. _____

**1.** Write the numbers in *decreasing* order.

$$-\frac{3}{2}, 0, \frac{2}{3}, -\frac{2}{3}, -\frac{5}{2}, \frac{1}{5}$$

1. _____

**2.** Graph the numbers, $-1.5$ and $-2.5$, on the number line. Which is greater?

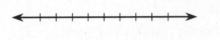

2. _____
*Use graph at left.*

**3.** Find the opposite of the number $\left|-\frac{6}{5}\right|$.

3. _____

**4.** Evaluate the expression $\left|-\frac{5}{2}\right| - \left|\frac{5}{2}\right|$.

4. _____

**5.** Evaluate the sum $28.97 + (-7.29) + |-5.31|$.

5. _____

**6.** Simplify the expression $-7 + x + (2x - 7)$.

6. _____

**7.** Evaluate the expression $17 - (-x) - |-10|$ when $x = 3$.

7. _____

**8.** Find the sum of the matrices $\begin{bmatrix} -5 & -4 \\ -3 & -2 \\ -1 & 0 \end{bmatrix} + \begin{bmatrix} 0 & -1 \\ -2 & -3 \\ -4 & -5 \end{bmatrix}$.

8. _____

9. Find the difference of the matrices $\begin{bmatrix} 8 & -12 \\ 7 & -2 \end{bmatrix} - \begin{bmatrix} -3 & -5 \\ -4 & 2 \end{bmatrix}$.

9. _____

10. Find the product $(-8x)|10|(2x)$.

10. _____

11. Find the product to 2 decimal places.

$(-8.66)(1.72)(-3.24)$

11. _____

12. **Shirt Purchase**    A man buys 6 shirts at $16 each.  There is also a 6% sales tax.  Find his total bill.

12. _____

13. Evaluate the expression $-5x(|x - 7|)$ when $x = -3$.

13. _____

14. **Sales Commission**    A salesman gets a commission of $2.65 on each item sold.  One morning he sold 15 calculators and 19 pocket radios. Find his commission.

14. _____

15. Simplify the expression $x(2 - x) - x(3 - x)$.

15. _____

16. **Buying Clothes**   You have $40.00. You wish to buy a T-shirt costing $14.50. You would also like to buy a pair of jeans. There is a 6% sales tax on clothing. What is the top tag price (excludes sales tax) you could pay for the jeans?

16. _____

17. Remove parentheses by applying the Distributive Property.

$$3x^2(4 - x^2)$$

17. _____

18. Simplify the quotient $\dfrac{-42 - 18x}{-6}$.

18. _____

19. Is $\dfrac{1.84 \text{ grams per } cm^3}{1.32 \text{ grams per } cm^3} \approx 1.39$ a rate or a ratio?

19. _____

20. **Gasoline Consumption**   A motorist travels 632 miles. Assuming the car averages 29.3 miles per gallon, how many gallons of gasoline (to the nearest tenth of a gallon) were used?

20. _____

Name _____

Date _____

**In 1–8, solve the equation.**

1. $6t = 21$

1. _____

2. $5 - m = 18$

2. _____

3. $\dfrac{2x}{5} = \dfrac{7}{4}$

3. _____

4. $2y + \frac{3}{2} = 1 - y$

4. _____

5. $\frac{2}{3}(x - 2) = 16$

5. _____

6. $5d - 4 = 3d + 7$

6. _____

7. $2(3 - x) = 3(2 - x)$

7. _____

8. $5(x - |-2|) = -|-3|$

8. _____

9. **Cartons of Film**   Film is packaged 12 rolls to a carton and retails at $2 per roll. A store's order has a retail value of $96. How many cartons of film did they order?

9. _____

10. **Two Cars**   Two cars are 2 miles apart on a straight road, traveling in the same direction. The lead car travels at 25 mph and the trailing car travels at 35 mph. How long does it take the faster car to catch the slower car?

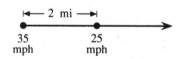

10. _____

**In 1–8, solve the equation.**

1. $8t = 34$

2. $13 - N = -28$

3. $\frac{4}{3}x = \frac{2}{9}$

4. $3y - \frac{2}{3} = 1 + y$

5. $\frac{3}{5}(x - 4) = 9$

6. $7d - 3 = 5d + 4$

7. $5(4 - 2x) = 7(3 + x)$

8. $9(|-2| - x) = -|-5|$

1. _____

2. _____

3. _____

4. _____

5. _____

6. _____

7. _____

8. _____

9. **Cartons of Film**   Film is packaged 12 rolls to a carton and retails at $2.50 per roll. A store's order has a retail value of $150. How many cartons of film did they order?

9. _____

10. **Two Cars**   Two cars are $D$ miles apart on a straight road, traveling in the same direction. The lead car travels at 25 miles per hour and the trailing car travels at 35 mph. The faster car overtakes the slower one in 12 minutes ($\frac{1}{5}$ hour). Find the distance, $D$, they were apart.

35 mph     25 mph

10. _____

**In 1–8, solve the equation.**

1. $4x = 20$

    1. _____

2. $\dfrac{x}{5} = 3$

    2. _____

3. $3x + 5 = 26$

    3. _____

4. $\dfrac{y + 1}{2} = 9$

    4. _____

5. $5n - 2(n - 2) = -11$

    5. _____

6. $6z + 3 = 8z - 5$

    6. _____

7. $5x + 14 - 2x = 9 - (4x + 2)$

    7. _____

8. $(5 \div 2) - x(x + 1) = x(2 - x)$

    8. _____

**In 9 and 10, solve the equation. Round your result to two decimal places.**

9. $\dfrac{14x}{5} + 7x = 23$

9. _____

10. $14.2y - 12.5 = 6.4y - 13.7$

10. _____

11. Solve for $t$ in the equation.

$$5st + 4 = 3s$$

11. _____

12. Solve for $m$ in the equation.

$$5nm + n = 3m$$

12. _____

13. **Geometry**  The triangle at the right has a perimeter of 20. Solve for $x$.

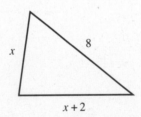

13. _____

14. **Geometry**  The circle at the right has a circumference of 16 inches. Approximate the radius of the circle. Round your result to two decimal places.

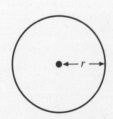

14. _____

15. **Video Clubs**   One video rental club charges $25 to become a member and $2.50 to rent each video. Another charges no rental fee, but charges $3.25 to rent each video. How many videos must you rent to make the first club more economical?

15. _____

16. Write the ordered pairs that are represented by the points in the coordinate plane at the right.

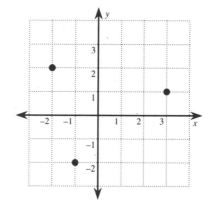

16. _____

17. Plot the points (3, 0), (2, −3), and (−2, −2).

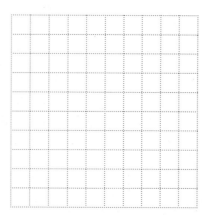

17.   *Use graph at left.*

18. **Holstein Calves**   The weights of ten Holstein calves, of different ages, are given in the table. Sketch a scatter plot of the data. Then describe any pattern that you see in the scatter plot.

18. _____
    *Use graph at left.*

| Age (months) | Weight (pounds) |
|---|---|
| 2 | 225 |
| 2 | 245 |
| 3 | 350 |
| 5 | 610 |
| 6 | 700 |
| 8 | 940 |
| 8 | 970 |
| 9 | 1040 |
| 10 | 1220 |
| 10 | 1260 |

# Chapter 3 Test

## Form B

(Page 1 of 3 pages)

Name ______________________

Date ______________________

**In 1–8, solve the equation.**

**1.** $8x = 44$ **1.** ______________

**2.** $\frac{x}{7} = 8$ **2.** ______________

**3.** $4x + 8 = 21$ **3.** ______________

**4.** $\frac{y+3}{4} = 7$ **4.** ______________

**5.** $4n - 2(3 - n) = -13$ **5.** ______________

**6.** $7z + 5 = 9z - 3$ **6.** ______________

**7.** $3x + 17 - 5x = 12 - (6x + 3)$ **7.** ______________

**8.** $(7 \div 3) + x(x - 1) = x(x - 2)$ **8.** ______________

**In 9 and 10, solve the equation. Round your result to two decimal places.**

9. $\dfrac{13x}{7} + 5x = 15$

9. _____

10. $18.3y - 7.6 = 8.4y - 14.6$

10. _____

11. Solve for $t$ in the equation.

$$7st + 13 = 2s$$

11. _____

12. Solve for $m$ in the equation.

$$6nm + 5n = 4m$$

12. _____

13. **Geometry**   The triangle at the right has a perimeter of 23.2. Solve for $x$.

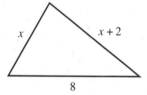

13. _____

14. **Geometry**   The circle at the right has a circumference of 27 inches. Approximate the radius of the circle to two decimal places.

14. _____

**15. Video Clubs**   One video rental club charges $20 to become a member and $2.50 to rent each video. Another charges no rental fee, but charges $3.25 to rent each video. How many videos must you rent to make the first club more economical?

15. _____

**16.** Write the ordered pairs that are represented by the points in the coordinate plane at the right.

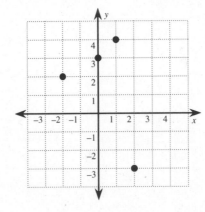

16. _____

**17.** Plot the points (4, 0), (−2, −3), (3, 1), and (−2, 2).

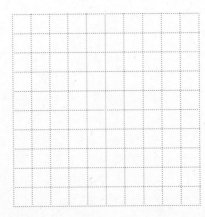

17.   *Use graph at left.*

**18. Holstein Calves**   The weights of ten Holstein calves, of different ages, are given in the table. Sketch a scatter plot of the data. Then describe any pattern that you see in the scatter plot.

| Age (months) | Weight (pounds) |
|---|---|
| 2 | 230 |
| 2 | 250 |
| 3 | 320 |
| 5 | 590 |
| 6 | 680 |
| 8 | 920 |
| 8 | 960 |
| 9 | 1020 |
| 10 | 1250 |
| 12 | 1350 |

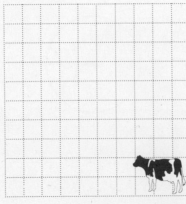

18. _____
   *Use graph at left.*

# Chapter 3 Test

## Form C

(Page 1 of 3 pages)

Name ______________________

Date ______________________

**In 1–8, solve the equation.**

**1.** $-7x = |-28|$ **1.** ____________

**2.** $\frac{x}{2} + \frac{x}{4} = 5$ **2.** ____________

**3.** $2x - |-5| = 23$ **3.** ____________

**4.** $\frac{3y + 2}{4} = 7$ **4.** ____________

**5.** $|5|n - 2(2 - n) = -7$ **5.** ____________

**6.** $3 - 4z = -5 + 8z$ **6.** ____________

**7.** $7x - 29 - 21x = 3 - (12 + 2x)$ **7.** ____________

**8.** $x(2x - 1) - 10 = -2x(1 - x)$ **8.** ____________

**In 9 and 10, solve the equation. Round your result to two decimal places.**

9. $\dfrac{11x}{3} + 11x = 23$

9. _____

10. $27.4y - 11.2 = 7.3y - 12.6$

10. _____

11. Solve for $t$ in the equation.

$$\dfrac{7s - 2st}{3} = 4$$

11. _____

12. Solve for $m$ in the equation.

$$\dfrac{5m + 2mn}{7} = 12$$

12. _____

13. **Geometry**   The trapezoid at the right has a perimeter of 20. Solve for $x$.

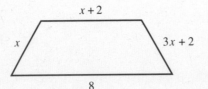

13. _____

14. **Geometry**   The circle at the right has a circumference of 21.54 inches. Approximate the radius of the circle to two decimal places.

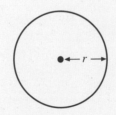

14. _____

**15.** *Video Clubs*    One video rental club charges $25 to become a member and $1.80 to rent each video. Another charges no rental fee, but charges $3.20 to rent each video. How many videos must you rent to make the first club more economical?

15. _____

**16.** Write the ordered pairs that are represented by the points in the coordinate plane at the right.

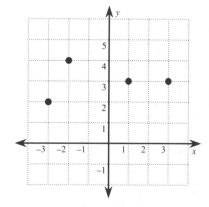

16. _____

**17.** Plot the points $(0, 3)$, $(2, -3)$, $(-3, 1)$, and $(-2, 2)$.

17.    *Use graph at left.*

**18.** *Holstein Calves*    The weights of ten Holstein calves, of different ages, are given in the table. Sketch a scatter plot of the data. Then describe any pattern that you see in the scatter plot.

| Age (months) | Weight (pounds) |
|---|---|
| 2 | 240 |
| 3 | 350 |
| 3 | 370 |
| 4 | 510 |
| 6 | 690 |
| 6 | 700 |
| 7 | 800 |
| 8 | 940 |
| 8 | 980 |
| 10 | 1250 |
| 12 | 1300 |

18. _____
   *Use graph at left.*

1. What is the quotient of 35 and 14?

   1. _____

2. Evaluate $[29.3 - (17.2 \div 14.7)] + (2.3)(7.7)$ to two decimal places.

   2. _____

3. *Geometry*  Find the perimeter of the rectangle shown.

   18.16

   25.72

   3. _____

4. *Geometry*  A rectangle is three times as long as it is wide and its longer side is 21.3 inches. Find its perimeter.

   4. _____

5. Evaluate $7z + (6 - 2z)$ when $z = 7$.

   5. _____

6. Write a variable expression for "the product of a number $x$ and 12, divided by the sum of the number $x$ and 2."

   6. _____

7. **Geometry**   The area of a circle is $\pi$ times the square of the radius, where $\pi \approx 3.14$. Find the area of a circle whose radius is 9.23 to two decimal places.

7. _____

8. **Geometry**   Find the volume of a cube whose side length is 9.

8. _____

9. Evaluate the expression $38x + 12 - x^3$ when $x = 2$.

9. _____

10. Evaluate $[(t + 3)^2 - 5^2] \div 3$ when $t = 4$.

10. _____

11. Is $x = 5$ a solution of the equation $3x - 7 = x + 3$?

11. _____

12. Is $x = 7$ a solution of the inequality $19 - 2x \geq 27 - 3x$?

12. _____

13. Write an equation or inequality for the verbal statement "the product of 3 and a number $B$ is not less than 10."

13. _____

14. **Bus Reservations**  A bus excursion costs $275 plus $12 for each person making reservations. The total bill is $731. How many people made reservations?

14. _____

15. **Company Sales**  A company makes products $A$ and $B$. The sales of the two products in thousands of units are shown in the bar graph for the years 1985 and 1990. Find the percent increase in the sales of product $B$ during that time period.

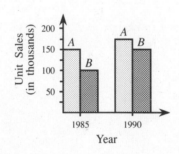

15. _____

16. Rewrite the numbers in *increasing* order.

$-\frac{7}{3}, \frac{3}{7}, 0, \frac{5}{6}, \frac{1}{8}, -\frac{4}{5}$

16. _____

17. Find the opposite of the number $\left|-\frac{2}{3}\right|$.

17. _____

**18.** Evaluate the expression $-\frac{1}{2} - \left|-\frac{1}{2}\right|$.

18. _____

**19.** Evaluate $28.12 + |-17.28| + (-16.18)$.

19. _____

**20.** Simplify the expression $-8 - (-6) + [-(5 - 3)]$.

20. _____

**21.** Evaluate the expression $|-25| - |10 - x|$ when $x = 5$.

21. _____

**22.** Find the sum of the matrices $\begin{bmatrix} 2 & 1 & 4 \\ 1 & -2 & 3 \end{bmatrix} + \begin{bmatrix} 8 & -2 & 3 \\ 7 & 0 & 5 \end{bmatrix}$.

22. _____

**23.** Find the difference of the matrices

$$\begin{bmatrix} 3 & 1 & 2 & 4 \\ 1 & 4 & -1 & 5 \end{bmatrix} - \begin{bmatrix} 1 & 5 & 7 & -2 \\ -3 & 0 & 4 & -1 \end{bmatrix}.$$

23. _____

**24.** Find the product to two decimal places.

$(8.75)(-13.31)(4.23)$

24. _____

**25.** *Wholesale Price*   A brand of skirts wholesales at $47.25 each in lots of 12 or more. Find the wholesale price for 18 skirts.

25. _____

**26.** Evaluate the expression  $13 - 7x - 2x^2$  when $x = -4$.

26. _____

**27.** Simplify the expression  $5(|-2| - x) - 3(3 - 2x)$.

27. _____

**28.** *Buying Two Items*   You have $50.00. You wish to buy a calculator that costs $14.95 and a cassette player on sale at $32.50. There is a six percent sales tax. Do you have enough money to pay for both?

28. _____

**29.** Simplify the quotient  $\dfrac{42 - 35x}{7}$.

29. _____

**30.** Which is a ratio?

$$\frac{375 \ \text{dollars}}{21.3 \ \text{pounds}} \approx 17.61 \ \text{dollars per pound, or}$$

$$\frac{1.93 \ \text{lbs}}{1.80 \ \text{lbs}} \approx 1.07$$

30. _____

31. ***Gasoline Use***   A motorist expects to travel 783 miles. Her car averages 31.2 miles per gallon for highway driving. How many gallons of gasoline (to the nearest 0.1 gallon) should she anticipate using?

31. _____

32. Solve the equation $5x - 7 = x + 21$.

32. _____

33. Solve the equation $7n - 3(2 - n) = 54$.

33. _____

34. Solve the equation $\dfrac{9 - 3y}{4} = 9$.

34. _____

35. Solve the equation $3z - 2(z + 6) = 3(z - 2)$.

35. _____

36. Solve the equation $x(3 - x) = -x(x - 2) + (5 \div 2)$.

36. _____

**37.** Solve the equation. Round your answer to two decimal places.

$$2.31y - 11.21 = 7.33y - 14.80$$

37. _____

**38. *Geometry*** The rectangle at the right has a perimeter of 30. Solve for $x$.

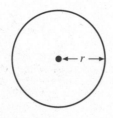

$x - 3$

$x + 2$

38. _____

**39. *Geometry*** The circle at the right has a circumference of 20 inches. Find its area to two decimal places.

$\bullet \leftarrow r \rightarrow$

39. _____

**40.** Solve the equation for $R$.   $10RT + 2T = 3R$

40. _____

**41.** Write the ordered pairs that are represented by the points in the coordinate plane at the right.

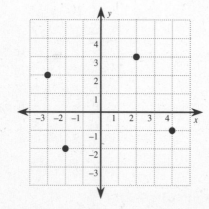

41. _____

**42.** Plot the points

$(-2,\ 0), (4,\ -2), (-1,\ -3)$, and $(0,\ 1)$.

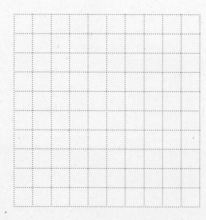

42.   *Use graph at left.*

**43.** *Retail Sales*   Estimate the retail sales for October of 1991.

**43.** _____

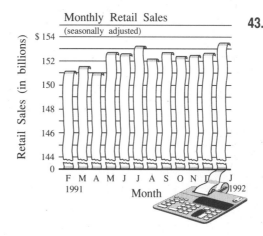

Monthly Retail Sales
(seasonally adjusted)

Retail Sales (in billions)

Month

1991                    1992

**44.** *Earnings and Revenue*   Compare Ford's performances in 1987 and 1991.

**44.** _____

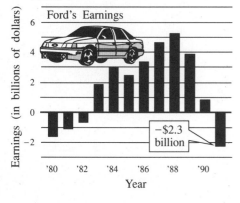

Ford's Earnings

Earnings (in billions of dollars)

−$2.3 billion

Year

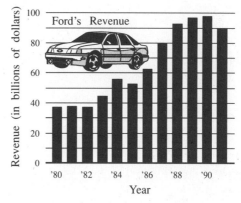

Ford's Revenue

Revenue (in billions of dollars)

Year

Name _____

Date _____

**Use a straightedge to draw straight lines on graphs.**

**1.** Write an equation for the graph of a line for which the $x$-coordinate of each point is 2.

1. _____

**2.** Write the equation of the horizontal line which passes through the point $(7, -1)$.

2. _____

**3.** Use a table of values to sketch the graph of $x + 2y = 4$.

| $x$ | | | |
|---|---|---|---|
| $y$ | | | |

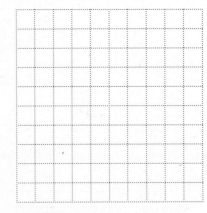

3.   *Use graph at left.*

**4.** Which of the two points lies on the graph of the line $3x - 2y = 6$?

$\left(3, \frac{3}{2}\right)$ or $\left(\frac{2}{3}, \frac{3}{2}\right)$

4. _____

**5.** *Toys and Sports*   The amount, $y$, spent on nondurable toys and sports supplies increased at a linear rate from \$14.6 billion in 1980 to \$31.2 billion in 1990. Sketch the line showing the amount spent from 1980 to 1990. (Let $t = 0$ represent 1980.) What was the average rate of change over the 10-year period?

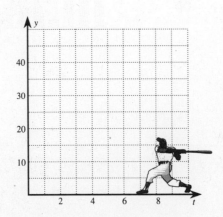

5.   *Use graph at left.*

**6.** Find the slope of the line passing through the points $(1, 3)$ and $(3, -3)$.

6. _____

**7.** Find the *rate of change* between the two points. Give the *unit of measure*. $x$ is measured in dozens; $y$ is measured in dollars; $(3, 14)$, $(10, 63)$.

7. _____

   *Algebra 1*

**Use a straightedge to draw straight lines on graphs.**

1. Write an equation for the graph of a line for which the $y$-coordinate of each point is $-3$.

1. _____

2. Write the equation of the vertical line which passes through the point $(7,\ -1)$.

2. _____

3. Use a table of values to sketch the graph of $2x - y = 4$.

| x | | | |
|---|---|---|---|
| y | | | |

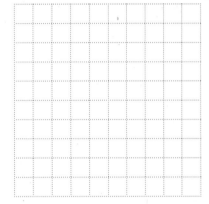

3. *Use graph at left.*

4. Which of the two points lies on the graph of the line $3x + 2y = 6$?

$\left(3,\ \frac{3}{2}\right)$ or $\left(\frac{2}{3},\ 2\right)$

4. _____

5. **Toys and Sports** The amount, $y$, spent on durable toys and sports equipment increased at a linear rate from $17.2 billion in 1980 to $39.1 billion in 1990. Sketch the line showing the amount spent from 1980 to 1990. (Let $t = 0$ represent 1980.) What was the average rate of change over the 10-year period?

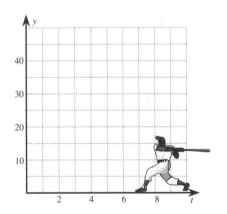

5. *Use graph at left.*

6. Find the slope of the line passing through the points $(3,\ 3)$ and $(-2,\ 4)$

6. _____

7. Find the *rate of change* between the two points. Give the *unit of measure*. $x$ is measured in minutes; $y$ is measured in yards; $(2,\ 21),\ (7,\ 46)$.

7. _____

1. Sketch the graphs of $x = -3$ and $y = 4$. Find the point at which the two graphs intersect.

   1. _____
   *Use graph at left.*

2. Write the equation of the line passing through $(2, -7), (2, 0),$ and $(2, 5)$.

   2. _____

3. Write the equation of the horizontal line passing through the point $(4, 7)$.

   3. _____

4. Which point, $\left(\frac{5}{2}, 3\right)$ or $\left(\frac{3}{2}, 2\right)$, is on the graph of $2x - \frac{2}{3}y = 3$?

   4. _____

5. Complete the table.

   5. _____

| $x$ | $-3$ | $-1$ | 0 | 2 | 4 |
| --- | --- | --- | --- | --- | --- |
| $y = \frac{1}{2}x - 4$ | | | | | |

6. Find the $x$-intercept of the line $3x - 4y = 12$.

   6. _____

7. **School Enrollment** For 1980 through 1990, Brentwood Middle School's enrollment, $y$, was related to the year, $t$, by the equation $y = 240 + 20t$, where $t = 0$ represents 1980. Sketch the graph of this equation.

   7. *Use graph at left.*

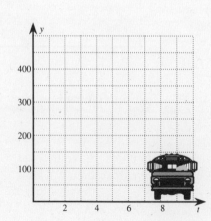

ⓒ D. C. Heath and Company *Algebra 1*

**8.** Plot the points and find the slope of the line passing through the points $(3, \ -5)$ and $(5, \ 4)$.

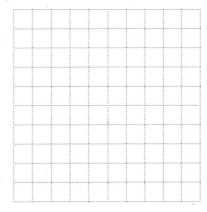

**8.** _____
*Use graph at left.*

**9.** Find the *rate of change* between the two points $(5, \ 78)$ and $(9, \ 92)$ and give the *unit of measure*. $x$ is measured in hours; $y$ is measured in degrees.

**9.** _____

**10.** Find the slope of the line through the points $(-1, \ -3)$ and $(-1, \ 7)$.

**10.** _____

**11.** *Savings Account*   On January 1, Mario had a savings account balance of \$2742 and by April 1, his balance had increased to \$3597. Find Mario's average savings rate in dollars per month for that period.

**11.** _____

**12.** Solve for $y$.   $4x - 5y = 0$

**12.** _____

**13.** Find the slope and $y$-intercept of the line.   $y = -7x + 15$

**13.** _____

**14.** Rewrite the equation in slope-intercept form.

$$5x - 2y - 7 = 0$$

14. _____

**15.** Solve the equation $5x - 7 = 4$.

15. _____

**16.** Write in slope-intercept form and sketch the line.

$$4x - y - 2 = 0$$

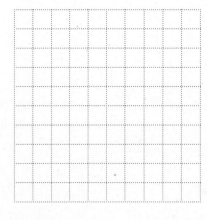

16. _____
*Use graph at left.*

**17.** Find the coordinates of the vertex of the graph.

$$y = |x - 3| + 2$$

17. _____

**18.** Sketch the graph $y = |x + 4|$.

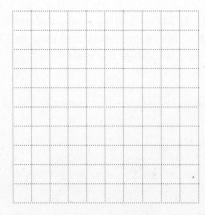

18. *Use graph at left.*

**19.** Solve the equation algebraically.

$$|x - 2| - 2 = 7$$

19. _____

**20.** *Liquid State*   Water is in a liquid state if its temperature, $t$ (in degrees Celcius), satisfies $|t - 50| < 50$. Find the two solutions of $|t - 50| = 50$. What do the solutions represent?

20. _____

**1.** Sketch the graphs of $x = -5$ and $y = 3$. Find the point at which the two graphs intersect.

1. _____
   *Use graph at left.*

**2.** Write the equation of the line passing through $(7, \ 1), (7, \ -4)$, and $(7, \ 4)$.

2. _____

**3.** Write the equation of the horizontal line passing through the point $(7, 4)$.

3. _____

**4.** Which point, $\left(\frac{5}{2}, \ 3\right)$ or $\left(\frac{3}{2}, \ 2\right)$, is on the graph of $2x - \frac{2}{3}y = \frac{5}{3}$?

4. _____

**5.** Complete the table.

5. _____

| x | −6 | −4 | −2 | 0 | 2 |
|---|---|---|---|---|---|
| $y = -\frac{1}{2}x - 1$ | | | | | |

**6.** Find the $y$-intercept of the line $3x - 4y = 12$.

6. _____

**7.** ***School Enrollment*** For 1980 through 1990, Sundale High School's enrollment, $y$, was related to the year, $t$, by the equation $y = 320 + 10t$, where $t = 0$ represents 1980. Sketch the graph of this equation.

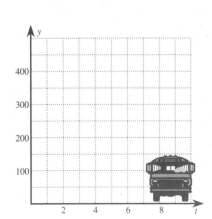

7. ___*Use graph at left.*___

8. Plot the points and find the
   slope of the line passing
   through the points $(-4,\ 2)$ and
   $(4,\ -3)$.

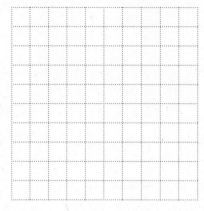

8. _____
   *Use graph at left.*

9. Find the *rate of change* between the two points $(10,\ 42)$ and
   $(13,\ 75)$ and give the *unit of measure*. $x$ is measured in hours; $y$ is
   measured in degrees.

9. _____

10. Find the slope of the line through the points $(4,\ 7)$ and $(-6,\ 2)$.

10. _____

11. **Savings Account**    On January 1, Muriel had a savings account
    balance of $1527 and by April 1, her balance had increased to
    $2478. Find Muriel's average savings rate in dollars per month for
    that period.

11. _____

12. Solve for $y$.   $7x + 2y = 0$

12. _____

13. Find the slope and $y$-intercept of the line.   $y = 7x - 15$

13. _____

**14.** Rewrite the equation in slope-intercept form.    **14.** _____

$$8x - 3y - 5 = 0$$

**15.** Solve the equation $11x - 3 = 16$.    **15.** _____

**16.** Write in slope-intercept form    **16.** _____
and sketch the line.    *Use graph at left.*

$$3x - y - 2 = 0$$

**17.** Find the coordinates of the vertex of the graph.    **17.** _____

$$y = |x - 4| - 3$$

**18.** Sketch the graph $y = |2 - x|$.    **18.** *Use graph at left.*

**19.** Solve the equation algebraically.    **19.** _____

$$15 - |x| = 7$$

**20.** *Liquid State*    Iodine is in a liquid state if its temperature, $t$ (in    **20.** _____
degrees Celcius), satisfies $|t - 149| < 35$. Find the two solutions
of $|t - 149| = 35$. What do the solutions represent?

**Form C**
(Page 1 of 3 pages)

Name _____

Date _____

1. Sketch the graphs of $x = -2$ and $y = -4$. Find the point at which the two graphs intersect.

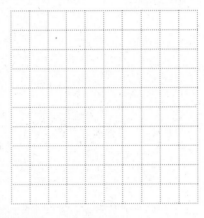

1. _____
   *Use graph at left.*

2. Write the equation of the line passing through $(1, -2), (5, -2)$, and $(10, -2)$.

2. _____

3. Write the equation of the vertical line passing through the point $(-5, 2)$.

3. _____

4. Which point, $\left(\frac{5}{2}, -3\right)$ or $\left(-\frac{3}{2}, 6\right)$, is on the graph of $2x - \frac{2}{3}y = -7$?

4. _____

5. Complete the table.

5. _____

| $x$ | $-3$ | $-2$ | 0 | 2 | 3 |
|-----|------|------|---|---|---|
| $y = -\frac{1}{3}x + 5$ | | | | | |

6. Find both intercepts of the line $3x + 4y = -12$.

6. _____

7. **School Enrollment** For 1980 through 1990, Cross Creek High School's enrollment, $y$, was related to the year, $t$, by the equation $y - 25t - 425 = 0$, where $t = 0$ represents 1980. Sketch the graph of this equation.

7. *Use graph at left.*

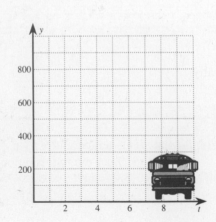

*Algebra 1*

**8.** Plot the points and find the slope of the line passing through the points $(\frac{9}{2}, \ 2)$ and $(-3, \ -\frac{3}{2})$.

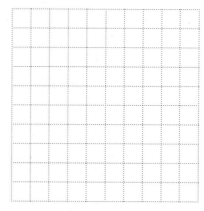

8. _____
   *Use graph at left.*

**9.** Find the *rate of change* between the two points $(3, \ 73)$ and $(12, \ 40)$ and give the *unit of measure*. $x$ is measured in hours; $y$ is measured in degrees.

9. _____

**10.** Find the slope of the line through the points $(-6, \ 7)$ and $(\frac{5}{2}, \ 1)$.

10. _____

**11.** *Savings Account*  On January 1, Marian received a trust fund worth $10,721. On April 1, her balance was $7028. Ignoring interest, find Marian's spending rate in dollars per month for that period.

11. _____

**12.** Solve for $y$.  $5x - 4y = 12$

12. _____

**13.** Find the slope and $y$-intercept of the line.  $2x - 5y = 10$

13. _____

**14.** Rewrite the equation in slope-intercept form.

$\frac{1}{3}x - 2y + \frac{2}{3} = 0$

14. _____

**15.** Solve the equation $25x - 11 = 54$.

15. _____

**16.** Write in slope-intercept form and sketch the line.

$4x + 3y - 8 = 0$

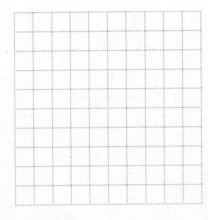

16. _____
*Use graph at left.*

**17.** Find the coordinates of the vertex of the graph.

$y = |5 - x| - \frac{1}{2}$

17. _____

**18.** Sketch the graph $y = |x| - 3$.

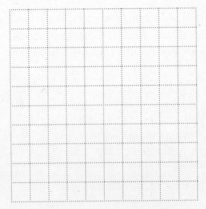

18. *Use graph at left.* _____

**19.** Solve the equation algebraically.

$3 + |x - 3| = 7$

19. _____

**20.** *Liquid State*    Ethol alcohol is in a liquid state if its temperature, $t$ (in degrees Celcius), satisfies $|t + 19| < 98$. Find the two solutions of $|t + 19| = 98$. What do the solutions represent?

20. _____

Name

Date _____

1. The slope is 5 and the $y$-intercept is $-\frac{1}{2}$. Write the equation of the line.

   1. _____

2. Write an equation of the line shown on the graph.

   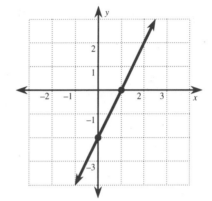

   2. _____

3. **Taxi Ride**   A taxicab charges \$2.50 plus \$1.25 for each $\frac{1}{4}$th mile. Write a linear model that gives the total cost, $y$, for a trip of $x$ miles.

   3. _____

4. Write the slope-intercept form of the equation of the line that passes through the point $(1, \ -4)$ with a slope of $\frac{2}{3}$.

   4. _____

5. Find an equation of the line that crosses the $x$-axis at $(-2, \ 0)$ with a slope of 4.

   5. _____

6. Write the slope-intercept form of the equation of the line that passes through the points $(-1, \ 4)$ and $(3, \ 0)$.

   6. _____

7. Write an equation of the line whose $x$-intercept is $-4$ and whose $y$-intercept is $-2$.

   7. _____

8. **Collie Puppies**   In the table, $x$ represents the age of a female collie and $y$ represents the total number of puppies she has had. Construct a scatter plot for this data and find an equation you think best represents the data.

   8. _____
   *Use graph at left.*

| x | 1 | 2 | 3 | 4 | 5 | 6 | 7 | 8 |
|---|---|---|----|----|----|----|----|----|
| y | 6 | 8 | 15 | 19 | 27 | 31 | 35 | 39 |

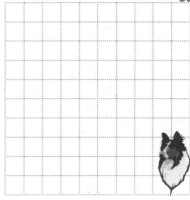

Name _____

Date _____

1. The slope is $-\frac{1}{2}$ and the $y$-intercept is 5. Write the equation of the line.

   1. _____

2. Write an equation of the line shown on the graph.

   2. _____

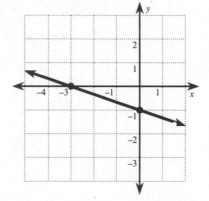

3. **Taxi Ride** A taxicab charges $2.75 plus $0.40 for each $\frac{1}{10}$th mile. Write a linear model that gives the total cost, $y$, for a trip of $x$ miles.

   3. _____

4. Write the slope-intercept form of the equation of the line that passes through the point $(-2, 3)$ with a slope of $-\frac{1}{4}$.

   4. _____

5. Find an equation of the line that crosses the $x$-axis at $(-4, 0)$ with a slope of 2.

   5. _____

6. Write the slope-intercept form of the equation of the line that passes through the points $(1, -2)$ and $(2, 0)$.

   6. _____

7. Write an equation of the line whose $x$-intercept is $-3$ and whose $y$-intercept is $-2$.

   7. _____

8. **Biking** In the table, $x$ represents the number of hours you have been mountain biking and $y$ represents the number of miles you are from home. Construct a scatter plot for this data and find an equation you think best represents the data.

   8. _____
   *Use graph at left.*

| x | 1 | 2 | 3 | 4 | 5 | 6 | 7 | 8 |
|---|---|---|---|---|---|---|---|---|
| y | 35 | 29 | 26 | 20 | 16 | 9 | 6 | 0 |

1. Write an equation of the line whose slope is $\frac{1}{3}$ and whose $y$-intercept is $-4$.

   1. _____

2. Write an equation of the line shown on the graph.

   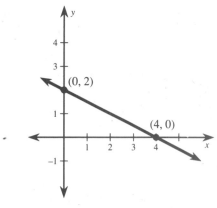

   2. _____

3. Find an equation of a line that passes through the point $(3, -1)$ with a slope of 3.

   3. _____

4. A line passes through point $(-2, -2)$ and has a slope of 2. Sketch the line and write its equation in slope-intercept form.

   4. _____
   *Use graph at left.*

5. Write the equation of the line in slope-intercept form that passes through the points $(7, -1)$ and $(2, 9)$.

   5. _____

6. Sketch the line given by $3x - 4y = -12$. Label the $x$- and $y$- intercepts.

   6. _*Use graph at left.*_

7. Write the equation of the horizontal line that passes through the point (7, −3).

7. _____

8. **Summer Job**   In the table, $x$ represents the number of weeks you worked at a summer job and $y$ represents the balance in your savings account. Construct a scatter plot for this data and find an equation you think best represents the data.

8. _____
*Use graph at left.*

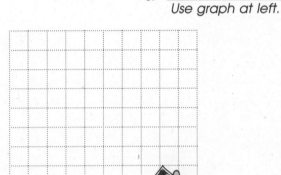

| x | 1 | 2 | 3 | 4 | 5 | 6 | 7 | 8 |
|---|---|---|---|---|---|---|---|---|
| y | 14 | 22 | 26 | 29 | 35 | 39 | 46 | 49 |

9. Rewrite the equation $y = -\frac{3}{4}x - \frac{1}{2}$ in *standard form* with integer coefficients.

9. _____

10. Which of the following lines are parallel to each other?

$7x + 3y = 1; \quad 7x - 3y = 2; \quad 7x + 3y = -2$

10. _____

11. Use the point-slope form to write an equation of the line that passes through the point $(-7, 1)$ with a slope of $\frac{1}{2}$.

11. _____

12. Write the equation $5y - 2x = 3$ in slope-intercept form.

12. _____

**13.** *Revenue*   A revenue of $1500 is obtained from the sales of item *A* at $50 each and item *B* at $25 each. Write an equation that shows the relationship between the numbers of items sold.

13. _____

**14.** *Airplane Trip*   An airplane is traveling away from its home airport at a constant speed. After 3 hours, it is 540 miles away. Assuming it departed at $t = 0$, write an equation representing the distance, $D$ (in miles), at any time $t$ (in hours).

14. _____

**15.** *Weekly Income*   A real estate sales agent receives a salary of $250 per week plus a commission of 2% of sales. Write a linear model for the weekly income $y$ in terms of sales $x$.

15. _____

**16.** *Depreciation*   Machinery is bought new for $36,000 and is considered worth $2000 as junk at the end of ten years. Assuming a linear model for depreciation, write the equation of its value, $V$ (in dollars), when $t$ years have elapsed after the purchase ($t \leq 10$).

16. _____

**Form B**

(Page 1 of 3 pages)

Name _____

Date _____

1. Write an equation of the line whose slope is $-\frac{3}{2}$ and whose
   $y$-intercept is $-5$.

   1. _____

2. Write an equation of the line
   shown on the graph.

   2. _____

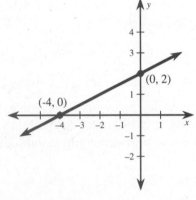

3. Find an equation of a line that passes through the point $(1, -4)$ with
   a slope of $-4$.

   3. _____

4. A line passes through point
   $(-1, -3)$ and has a slope of
   4. Sketch the line and write
   its equation in slope-intercept
   form.

   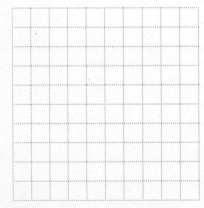

   4. _____
   *Use graph at left.*

5. Write the equation of the line in slope-intercept form that passes
   through the points $(-3, 5)$ and $(2, -5)$.

   5. _____

6. Sketch the line given by
   $4x + 3y = 12$. Label the $x$-
   and $y$- intercepts.

   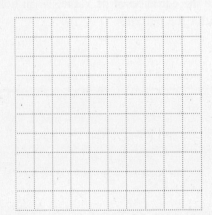

   6. *Use graph at left.* ____

*Algebra 1*

**7.** Write the equation of the vertical line that passes through the point (7, −3).

7. _____

**8.** *Water Consumption*   In the table, $x$ represents the number of hours you have worked at a lawn-mowing job and $y$ represents the number of ounces of water left in your water cooler. Construct a scatter plot for this data and find an equation you think best represents the data.

8. _____

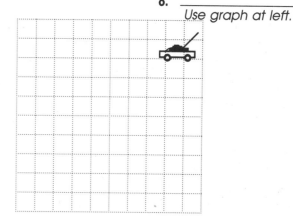

*Use graph at left.*

| x | 1 | 2 | 3 | 4 | 5 | 6 | 7 | 8 |
|---|---|---|---|---|---|---|---|---|
| y | 64 | 55 | 46 | 38 | 28 | 22 | 12 | 7 |

**9.** Rewrite the equation $y = \frac{2}{3}x - 4$ in *standard form* with integer coefficients.

9. _____

**10.** Which of the following lines are parallel to each other?

$$3x - 5y = 2; \quad 5x - 3y = 2; \quad 3x - 5y = -2$$

10. _____

**11.** Use the point-slope form to write an equation of the line that passes through the point (5, −7) with a slope of $\frac{3}{5}$.

11. _____

**12.** Write the equation $5x - 2y = 3$ in slope-intercept form.

12. _____

13. **Revenue**   A revenue of $1800 is obtained from the sales of item *A* at $30 each and item *B* at $90 each. Write an equation that shows the relationship between the numbers of items sold.

13. _____

14. **Airplane Trip**   An airplane leaves its home airport and travels away at a constant speed. $2\frac{1}{2}$ hours later it is 400 miles away. Write an equation giving its distance, *D* (in miles), at any time *t* (in hours).

14. _____

15. **Weekly Income**   A real estate sales agent receives a salary of $275 per week plus a commission of 1.5% of sales. Write a linear model for the weekly income of *y* in terms of sales *x*.

15. _____

16. **Depreciation**   Machinery is bought new for $75,000 and is considered worth $5000 as junk at the end of ten years. Assuming a linear model for depreciation, write the equation of its value, *V* (in dollars), when *t* years have elapsed after the purchase ($t \leq 10$).

16. _____

1. Write an equation of the line whose slope is $-\frac{1}{3}$ and whose $y$-intercept is $-3$.

   1. _____

2. Write an equation of the line shown on the graph.

   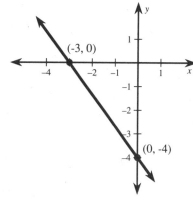

   2. _____

3. Find an equation of a line that passes through the point $(3, -2)$ with a slope of $\frac{3}{2}$.

   3. _____

4. A line passes through the point $(-1, -3)$ and has a slope of $\frac{3}{2}$. Sketch the line and write its equation in slope-intercept form.

   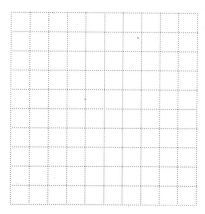

   4. _____
   *Use graph at left.*

5. Write the equation of the line in slope-intercept form that passes through the points $(7, -1)$ and $(2, 8)$.

   5. _____

6. Sketch the line given by $2x - 2y = 5$. Label the $x$- and $y$- intercepts.

   6. *Use graph at left.*

**7.** Write the equation of the vertical line that passes through the origin.

7. _____

**8.** ***Company Employees***   In the table, $x$ represents the number of years a company has been in business and $y$ represents the number of employees that the company has. Construct a scatter plot for this data and find an equation you think best represents the data.

8. _____
*Use graph at left.*

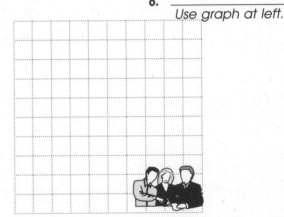

| x | 1 | 2 | 3 | 4 | 5 | 6 | 7 | 8 |
|---|---|---|---|---|---|---|---|---|
| y | 15 | 21 | 27 | 28 | 39 | 40 | 44 | 52 |

**9.** Rewrite the equation $\frac{x}{2} + \frac{y}{3} - 1 = 0$ in *standard form* with integer coefficients.

9. _____

**10.** Which of the following lines are parallel to each other?

$2x - 6y = 3; \quad 6x + 2y = 3; \quad -2x + 6y = 3$

10. _____

**11.** Use the point-slope form to write an equation of the line that passes through the point $\left(\frac{2}{3}, -\frac{3}{2}\right)$ with a slope of $-\frac{2}{3}$.

11. _____

**12.** Write the equation $y - 2 = -\frac{2}{3}(x + 6)$ in slope-intercept form.

12. _____

**13. Revenue**   Item $A$ sells for $24 each and item $B$ sells for $36 each. Combined sales of the two produce $2448 in revenue. Write an equation showing the relationship between the numbers of items sold.

13. _____

**14. Airplane Trip**   An airplane leaves its home airport and stops at another 90 miles away. Two hours after its initial departure it leaves the second airport and continues in the same direction at a constant rate. It is 410 miles from home 4 hours after its initial departure. Write an equation giving the distance, $D$ (in miles), in terms of the time $t$ (since initial departure) for the second leg of the trip.

14. _____

**15. Weekly Income**   A real estate sales agent receives a salary of $1500 per month plus a commission of 1% of sales. Write a linear model for the monthly income $y$ in terms of sales $x$.

15. _____

**16. Depreciation**   Machinery is bought new for $80,000 and is considered worth $15,000 as junk at the end of ten years. Assuming a linear model for depreciation, write the equation of its value, $V$ (in dollars), when $t$ years have elapsed after the purchase ($t \leq 10$).

16. _____

Name _____

Date _____

1. Sketch a graph of the inequality $x > -2$.

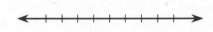

1. *Use graph at left.*

2. Solve the inequality $3 - 2x \leq 7 + x$.

2. _____

3. Write the inequality whose graph is at the right.

3. _____

4. Solve the inequality $2 + \frac{1}{3}x \geq 3$.

4. _____

5. Solve the inequality $-12 < 2 - x \leq 12$.

5. _____

6. Solve the inequality $4 \leq 2x < 10$.

6. _____

7. Write an inequality for the statement "$x$ is greater than or equal to 3 but less than 10."

7. _____

8. Graph the solution of the inequality $x < -3$ or $x > 4$.

8. *Use graph at left.*

9. **Fun Park Rides**   You have $12. A round trip bus ticket to a fun park is $1.20 and rides are $0.40 each. Write an inequality for the possible number of rides, $R$, you can afford.

9. _____

10. **Dimes and Quarters**   A pile of dimes and quarters totals $18 in value. If the number of dimes is at least 50, write an inequality describing the number of quarters, $Q$.

10. _____

   *Algebra 1*

1. Sketch a graph of the inequality $x \le 5$.

1. _Use graph at left._

2. Solve the inequality $3x - 5 > 2 - 5x$.

2. _____

3. Write the inequality whose graph is at the right.

3. _____

4. Solve the inequality $3 \le 1 + \frac{1}{2}x$.

4. _____

5. Solve the inequality $-13 \le 2 + x < 12$.

5. _____

6. Solve the inequality $6 < -3x \le 18$.

6. _____

7. Write an inequality for the statement "$x$ is greater than 2 but no greater than 5."

7. _____

8. Graph the solution of the inequality "$x$ is between $-3$ and 4."

8. _Use graph at left._

9. **Fun Park Rides**   You have $10. A round trip bus ticket to a fun park is $1.20 and rides are $0.40 each. Write an inequality for the possible number of rides, $R$, you can afford.

9. _____

10. **Dimes and Quarters**   A pile of dimes and quarters totals $15 in value. If the number of dimes is at least 30, write an inequality describing the number of quarters, $Q$.

10. _____

**Form A**
*(Page 1 of 3 pages)*

Name _____

Date _____

1. Solve the inequality $4 - 3x \geq x + 3$.

1. _____

2. Sketch a graph of the inequality $4 \leq x$.

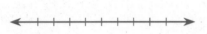

2. _Use graph at left._

3. Write the inequality whose graph is at the right.

3. _____

4. Solve the inequality $2 - \frac{1}{3}x > 3$.

4. _____

5. Solve the inequality $-2 < 1 + x \leq 2$.

5. _____

6. Solve the inequality $4 < 2(1 - 3x) < 10$.

6. _____

7. Write an inequality for the statement "$x$ is less than or equal to 5 and greater than or equal to 0."

7. _____

8. Graph the solution of $x < -1$ or $x > 3$.

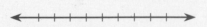

8. _Use graph at left._

ⓒ D.C. Heath and Company *Algebra 1*

9. **Reduced Rates**    Junior tickets to an event are available to teenagers
at reduced rates.  Write an inequality describing the age requirement
for a person of age $A$ who can buy a junior ticket.

9. _____

10. **Geometry**    Write a compound
inequality that gives the
possible lengths, $x$, of the side
of the triangle.

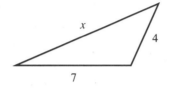

10. _____

11. Solve the inequality $|x - 3| \leq 4$.

11. _____

12. Sketch the graph of the
inequality $|2x - 1| < 3$.

12. _Use graph at left._

13. Is the ordered pair $(-3, \ 7)$ a solution of the inequality
$5x - 4y < -20$?

13. _____

14. Sketch a graph of the inequality
$3x - 2y \leq 6$.

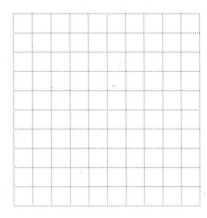

14. _Use graph at left._

**15.** *TVs and VCRs*   A wholesaler has $100,000 to spend on certain models of TV sets and VCRs. If the TV sets may be obtained at $415 each and the VCRs at $175 each, write an inequality that restricts the purchase of $x$ TVs and $y$ VCRs.

15. _____

**16.** $|x + 1| > 2$ is equivalent to which of the following?

   **a.** $-3 < x < 1$      **b.** $x > 1$ and $x < -3$

16. _____

**17.** Write an inequality to fit the graph at the right.

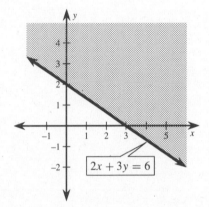

$2x + 3y = 6$

17. _____

**18.** *Industrial Production*   Use the bar graph to list the months in which the industrial production was greater than $106 billion but not greater than $107 billion.

18. _____

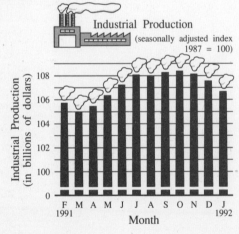

Industrial Production
(seasonally adjusted index
1987 = 100)

**1.** Solve the inequality $3 + 4x \leq x - 2$.

1. _____

**2.** Sketch a graph of the inequality $-3 \leq x$.

2. *Use graph at left.*

**3.** Write the inequality whose graph is at the right.

3. _____

**4.** Solve the inequality $9 + \frac{1}{2}x \leq 11$.

4. _____

**5.** Solve the inequality $-3 \geq 2x - 1 > -5$.

5. _____

**6.** Solve the inequality $-2 < -2x < 2$.

6. _____

**7.** Write an inequality for the statement "$x$ is between 3 and 7."

7. _____

**8.** Graph the solution of $|x| > 2$.

8. *Use graph at left.*

9. **Reduced Rates**   Junior tickets to an event are available to teenagers below age eighteen at reduced rates. Write an inequality describing the age requirement for a person of age $A$ who can buy a junior ticket.

9. _____

10. **Geometry**   Write a compound inequality that gives the possible lengths, $x$, of the side of the triangle.

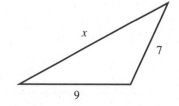

10. _____

11. Solve the inequality $|2 - x| \leq 2$.

11. _____

12. Sketch the graph of the inequality $|x| - 2 > 2$.

12. _Use graph at left._

13. Is the ordered pair $(2, -4)$ a solution of the inequality $2x - 4y > 20$?

13. _____

14. Sketch a graph of the inequality $-2x + 3y > 6$.

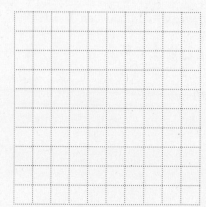

14. _Use graph at left._

ⓒ D. C. Heath and Company  *Algebra 1*

**15.** *TVs and VCRs*   A wholesaler has $75,000 to spend on certain models of TV sets and VCRs. If the TV sets may be obtained at $375 each and the VCRs at $215 each, write an inequality which restricts the purchase of $x$ TVs and $y$ VCRs.

15. _____

**16.** $|x - 1| > 4$ is equivalent to which of the following?
   **a.** $-3 < x < 5$     **b.** $x > 5$  and  $x < -3$

16. _____

**17.** Write an inequality to fit the graph at the right.

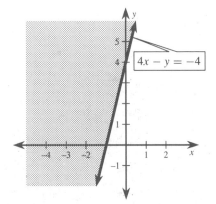

$4x - y = -4$

17. _____

**18.** *Industrial Production*   Use the bar graph to list the months in which the industrial production was less than $106 billion but not less than $105 billion.

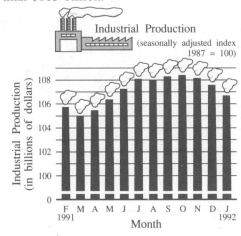

Industrial Production
(seasonally adjusted index
1987 = 100)

18. _____

**Form C**

*(Page 1 of 3 pages)*

Name _____

Date _____

1. Solve the inequality $2x + 4 > 1 - 2x$.

    1. _____

2. Sketch a graph of the inequality $x \geq -2$.

    2. *Use graph at left.*

3. Write the inequality whose graph is

    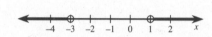

    3. _____

4. Solve the inequality $1 - \frac{1}{3}x > 3$.

    4. _____

5. Solve the inequality $-2 < 1 - 2x \leq 2$.

    5. _____

6. Solve the inequality $3 \leq 2 - x < 5$.

    6. _____

7. Write an inequality for the statement "$x$ is greater than or equal to 5 and less than or equal to 7."

    7. _____

8. Graph the solution to the inequality "$x$ is greater than 3 or less than or equal to 0."

    8. *Use graph at left.*

© D.C. Heath and Company *Algebra 1*

9. **Middleweight Division**    The middleweight division in a sport is centered at 160 pounds. Deviation from that must be less than 3 pounds either way. Write an inequality for the requirement on weight, $W$.

9. _____

10. **Geometry**    Write a compound inequality that gives the possible lengths, $x$, of the side of the triangle.

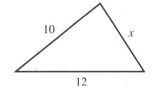

10. _____

11. Solve the inequality $|2 - \frac{1}{2}x| < 1$.

11. _____

12. Sketch the graph of the inequality $|2x - 1| > 3$.

12. _Use graph at left._

13. Is the ordered pair $(\frac{2}{3}, -\frac{3}{2})$ a solution of the inequality $3x - 2y \leq 5$?

13. _____

14. Sketch a graph of the inequality $2x - 3y \leq 6$.

14. _Use graph at left._

**15.** *Stock Purchase*    You have $4500 to buy stock and have decided on American Enterprises (AE) and Allied Junk Yards (AJY). AE sells for $27.50 per share and AJY sells for $45.25 per share. Write an inequality which restricts the purchase of *x* shares of AE and *y* shares of AJY.

**15.** _____

**16.** $|\frac{1}{2} - x| \leq \frac{2}{3}$ is equivalent to which of the following?

    **a.**  $(-\frac{7}{6} \leq x \leq \frac{1}{6})$  or **b.**  $(-\frac{1}{6} \leq x \leq \frac{7}{6})$

**16.** _____

**17.** Write an inequality to fit the graph at the right.

**17.** _____

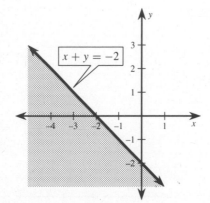

$x + y = -2$

**18.** *Industrial Production*    Use the bar graph to list the months in which the industrial production was greater than $107 billion but not greater than $108 billion.

**18.** _____

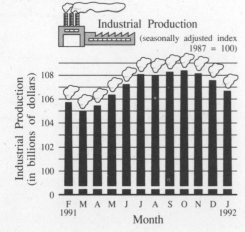

Industrial Production
(seasonally adjusted index
1987 = 100)

1. Evaluate $[12.44 - |-7.28|] \div [(3.17)(2.85)]$ to two decimal places.

1. _____

2. **Geometry** A rectangle is three times as long as it is wide and its shorter side is 12.71 inches. Find its perimeter to two decimal places.

2. _____

3. Write a variable expression for "the sum of a number $x$ and 7 is divided by the product of $x$ and 11."

3. _____

4. **Geometry** The area of a circle is $\pi$ times the square of the radius, where $\pi \approx 3.14$. Find the area of a circle whose radius is 11.73 to two decimal places.

4. _____

5. Evaluate the expression $72x + 15 - x^3$ when $x = -2$.

5. _____

6. Is $x = -6$ a solution of the inequality $23 - 3x \geq 18 + 4x$?

6. _____

**7.** Write an equation or inequality for the verbal statement "the product of $-4$ and a number $B$ is greater than or equal to 15."

7. _____

**8.** *Reception Cost*   A reception costs \$225 plus \$6 for each person making reservations. The total bill is \$1011. How many people made reservations?

8. _____

**9.** Find the sum of the matrices

$$\begin{bmatrix} 2 & -1 & 4 \\ 3 & 0 & 7 \end{bmatrix} + \begin{bmatrix} 1 & 5 & -2 \\ -3 & -2 & 4 \end{bmatrix}.$$

9. _____

**10.** *Sales Tax*   You have \$75.35. You wish to buy a calculator which costs \$18.95 and a cassette player priced at \$51.99. There is a six percent sales tax. Do you have enough money to pay for both?

10. _____

**11.** Simplify the quotient $\dfrac{30 - 21x}{3}$.

11. _____

**12.** Solve the equation $5N - 7(3 - 2N) = 36$.

12. _____

13. **Gasoline Consumption**    A motorist used 28.4 gallons of gasoline on a trip of 923 miles. Find the average gasoline consumption in miles per gallon to one decimal place.

13. _____

14. Solve the equation. Round your answer to two decimal places.

$$5.71x - 13.24 = 8.37x - 19.32$$

14. _____

15. **Geometry**    The circle at the right has a circumference of 25 inches. Find its area to two decimal places.

15. _____

16. Solve the equation for $A$.

$$12AB + 7B = 5A$$

16. _____

17. Write the equation of the horizontal line that passes through the point $(5, -4)$.

17. _____

**18.** *Chrysler's Revenue and Earnings*  Compare Chrysler's performances in 1986 and 1991.

18. _____

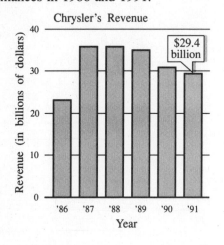

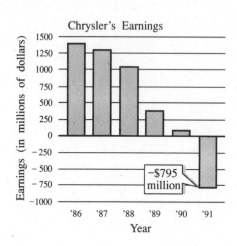

**19.** Find the slope and *y*-intercept of the line  $4x - 7y = 14$.

19. _____

**20.** Find the slope of the line containing the points  $(-3, \ 8)$ and $(5, \ 2)$.

20. _____

**21.** Sketch the graph and label the intercepts of the equation

$$5x - 3y = 30.$$

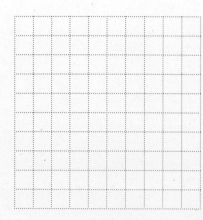

21. *Use graph at left.*

**22.** Complete the table for $y = \frac{2}{3}x - 5$.

| x | −6 | −3 | 0 | 3 | 6 | 9 |
|---|----|----|---|---|---|---|
| y |    |    |   |   |   |   |

**22.**  *Use table at left.*

**23.** Write the equation of the line passing through $(3,\ 7)$, $(-1,\ 7)$, and $(7,\ 7)$.

**23.** _____

**24.** Find the *rate of change* between the two points $(4,\ 36)$ and $(8,\ 108)$ and give the *unit of measure*.

   $x$ is measured in square yards.

   $y$ is measured in dollars.

**24.** _____

**25.** Solve for $y$.
$$5x - 13y = 0$$

**25.** _____

**26.** Write in slope-intercept form and sketch the line
$$3x - 2y = 12.$$

**26.** _____
*Use graph at left.*

**27.** Find the coordinates of the vertex of the graph $y = |x - 2| + 4$.

**27.** _____

**28.** Complete the table and sketch the graph of the equation $y = 3 - |x - 2|$.

| x | 0 | 1 | 2 | 3 | 4 |
|---|---|---|---|---|---|
| y |   |   |   |   |   |

**28.** *Use graph at left.* _____

**29.** Write an equation of the line shown in the graph.

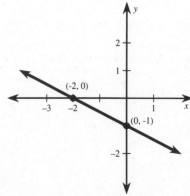

**29.** _____

**30.** Write in slope-intercept form the equation of the line through the points $(4, -1)$ and $(0, 3)$.

**30.** _____

**31.** Write in slope-intercept form the equation of the line through the points $(-5, 4)$ and $(7, -2)$.

**31.** _____

**32.** Construct a scatter plot for the data given and find an equation you think best represents the data.

**32.** _____
*Use graph at left.*

| x | −3 | −2 | −1 | 0 | 1 | 2 | 3 | 4 |
|---|---|---|---|---|---|---|---|---|
| y | −130 | −100 | −60 | −10 | 20 | 50 | 110 | 150 |

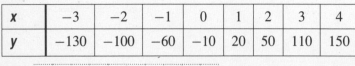

© D.C. Heath and Company  *Algebra 1*

**33.** *Salary Plus Commission*   A salesman receives a salary of $400 per week plus a commission of 5% of sales. Write a linear model for the weekly income $y$ in terms of sales $x$.

33. _____

**34.** Rewrite the equation $y = -\frac{6}{5}x + \frac{3}{2}$ in *standard form* with integer coefficients.

34. _____

**35.** Write the equation of the line that passes through the point $(4, -9)$ with slope $\frac{1}{5}$ in *point-slope form*.

35. _____

**36.** *Depreciation*   A heat exchanger is bought by a company for $180,000. It is considered to depreciate over 10 years to a scrap value of $10,000. Assuming a linear model for depreciation, write the equation of its value, $V$ (in dollars), when $t$ years have elapsed after the purchase ($t \leq 10$).

36. _____

**37.** Solve the inequality $5 - 7x < 12x + 40$.

37. _____

**38.** Write the inequality whose graph is at the right.

38. _____

**39.** Solve the inequality $\left| x - \frac{1}{2} \right| \geq \frac{2}{3}$.

39. _____

**40.** Is the ordered pair $(-7,\ 2)$ a solution of the inequality
$-3x + 7y \geq 6$?

40. _____

**41.** Sketch a graph of the inequality
$x - 2y < 2$.

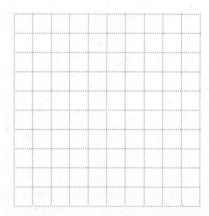

41. _Use graph at left._

**42.** Write an inequality to fit the
graph at the right.

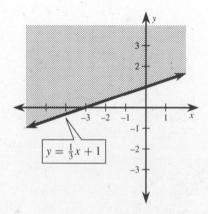

$y = \frac{1}{3}x + 1$

42. _____

**43. Stock Purchase**    A stock investor has $150,000 to invest in
two stocks.  APC, Inc. sells for $39.80 per share and Unified
Laboratories (UL) sells for $49.70 per share.  Write an inequality that
restricts an investment of $x$ shares of APC, Inc. and $y$ shares of UL.

43. _____

           *Algebra 1*

Name _____

Date _____

**Use a straightedge to draw straight lines.**

1. Decide whether $(3, -1)$ is a solution of the system.    1. _____
$$\begin{cases} 3x + y = 8 \\ -x + 2y = -5 \end{cases}$$

2. Decide whether $(2, 5)$ is a solution of the system.    2. _____
$$\begin{cases} 7x - 3y = -1 \\ 2x + 4y = 5 \end{cases}$$

3. Graph and check to solve the system.    3. _____
*Use graph at left.*
$$\begin{cases} x - y = 2 \\ 2x + y = 1 \end{cases}$$

**In 4 and 5, use substitution to solve the system.**

4. $\begin{cases} 3x + y = 0 \\ 5x + 2y = -2 \end{cases}$    4. _____

5. $\begin{cases} 2x + y = 1 \\ y = -x + 4 \end{cases}$    5. _____

**In 6 and 7, use linear combinations to solve the system.**

6. $\begin{cases} x - y = 3 \\ 2x + y = 6 \end{cases}$    6. _____

7. $\begin{cases} 2x + 3y = 5 \\ 3x + 2y = 0 \end{cases}$    7. _____

8. *Car Trip*   A car makes a trip of 435 miles in 8 hours. The car's    8. _____
average speed for the first part of the trip was 50 mph. For the rest
of the trip, the average speed was 60 mph. Find the times (in hours)
the car traveled at each speed.

Name _____

Date _____

**Use a straightedge to draw straight lines.**

1. Decide whether $(-2, 5)$ is a solution of the system.
$$\begin{cases} 7x + 3y = 1 \\ 2x - 4y = -5 \end{cases}$$

1. _____

2. Decide whether $(-3, 1)$ is a solution of the system.
$$\begin{cases} 3x + y = -8 \\ x - 2y = -5 \end{cases}$$

2. _____

3. Graph and check to solve the system.
$$\begin{cases} x + 2y = 4 \\ x - y = 1 \end{cases}$$

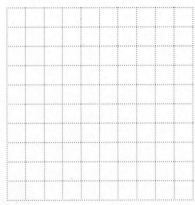

3. _____
*Use graph at left.*

**In 4 and 5, use substitution to solve the system.**

4. $\begin{cases} x + 3y = 3 \\ 2x + 3y = 0 \end{cases}$

4. _____

5. $\begin{cases} 2x + 3y = 5 \\ y = x - 5 \end{cases}$

5. _____

**In 6 and 7, use linear combinations to solve the system.**

6. $\begin{cases} x + y = 3 \\ 2x + y = -1 \end{cases}$

6. _____

7. $\begin{cases} 3x + 4y = -8 \\ x - 2y = 4 \end{cases}$

7. _____

8. *Car Trip*   A car makes a trip of 485 miles in 9 hours. The car's average speed for the first part of the trip was 60 mph. For the rest of the trip, the average speed was 50 mph. Find the times (in hours) the car traveled at each speed.

8. _____

In 1–3, describe whether the system graphically represents parallel lines, intersecting lines, or a single line. Also state whether the system has one solution, many solutions, or no solution.

1. $\begin{cases} 2x + 3y = 4 \\ 2x + 3y = 5 \end{cases}$

1. _____

2. $\begin{cases} x - 4y = 2 \\ 2x - 8y = 4 \end{cases}$

2. _____

3. $\begin{cases} x + y = 7 \\ x - y = 2 \end{cases}$

3. _____

**In 4, use a straightedge to draw straight lines.**

4. Solve the linear system by graphing.
$$\begin{cases} x + y = 1 \\ 3x - y = -5 \end{cases}$$

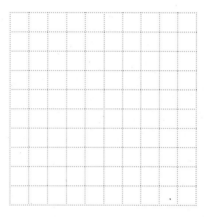

4. _____
*Use graph at left.*

5. Use substitution to solve the linear system.
$$\begin{cases} x + 4y = -1 \\ 2x - y = 7 \end{cases}$$

5. _____

6. Use linear combinations to solve the linear system.
$$\begin{cases} 3x - 4y = 21 \\ 4x + 2y = 6 \end{cases}$$

6. _____

7. Solve the linear system by any method.
$$\begin{cases} 3x - 2y = 3 \\ 6x + 2y = 3 \end{cases}$$

7. _____

8. Find the solution of the system, if it exists.

$$\begin{cases} 2x + 5y = 7 \\ -4x - 10y = 2 \end{cases}$$

8. _____

9. Find all solutions of the system.

$$\begin{cases} x + 2y = 4 \\ 2x + 4y = 8 \end{cases}$$

9. _____

10. **Annual Interest**  A total of $10,000 is invested in two funds paying 5% and 7% annual interest. The combined annual interest is $644. How much of the $10,000 is invested in each fund?

10. _____

11. **Salad Increments**  A salad contains $x$ pounds of ham and $y$ pounds of chicken. There are at most 4 pounds of ham and chicken in the salad. Write a system of inequalities to represent this situation. Sketch a graph of the system.

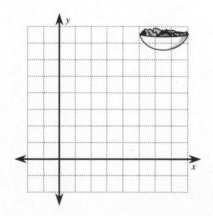

11. _____
*Use graph at left.*

12. Sketch the graph of the system of linear inequalities.

$$\begin{cases} y < \tfrac{1}{2}x \\ y > \tfrac{3}{2}x - 2 \end{cases}$$

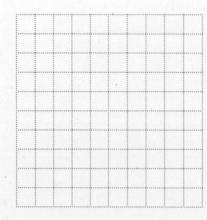

12. *Use graph at left.*

13. Sketch the graph of the constraints. Label the vertices of the graph.

$$\begin{cases} x + y \le 6 \\ x \quad\le 4 \\ \quad y \le 4 \\ x \quad\ge 0 \\ \quad y \ge 0 \end{cases}$$

13. _Use graph at left._

14. Find the *minimum* value of the objective quantity $C$.

$C = 2x - 7y$     Constraints:

$$\begin{cases} y \le 2x + 2 \\ x \le \quad 2 \\ y \ge \quad 0 \end{cases}$$

14. _____
_Use graph at left._

15. **Maximum Profit**     A manufacturer produces $x$ widgets and $y$ gidgets that have profits of $6 and $8 each, respectively. Each product goes through two processes with the required times as shown in the table. Find the daily production level for each product so that the profit is a maximum.

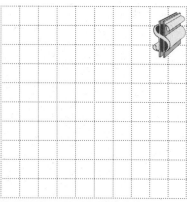

15. _____
_Use graph at left._

| Process | Hours to Produce a Widget | Hours to Produce a Gidget | Hours Available per Day |
|---------|---------------------------|---------------------------|-------------------------|
| I       | 1                         | 2                         | 10                      |
| II      | 2                         | 1                         | 8                       |

In 1–3, describe whether the system graphically represents parallel lines, intersecting lines, or a single line. Also state whether the system has one solution, many solutions, or no solution.

1. $\begin{cases} 2x - y = 5 \\ 4x - 2y = 10 \end{cases}$

1. _____

2. $\begin{cases} 2x - y = 1 \\ 2x + y = 1 \end{cases}$

2. _____

3. $\begin{cases} x + 4y = 7 \\ x + 4y = 6 \end{cases}$

3. _____

**In 4, use a straightedge to draw straight lines.**

4. Solve the linear system by graphing.
$\begin{cases} x - y = 1 \\ x + y = 3 \end{cases}$

4. _____
*Use graph at left.*

5. Use substitution to solve the linear system.
$\begin{cases} 3x - y = 15 \\ x + 2y = -2 \end{cases}$

5. _____

6. Use linear combinations to solve the linear system.
$\begin{cases} 4x + 3y = -2 \\ 3x + 2y = -3 \end{cases}$

6. _____

7. Solve the linear system by any method.
$\begin{cases} 5x - 2y = 3 \\ -x + 6y = -2 \end{cases}$

7. _____

**8.** Find the solution of the system, if it exists.

$$\begin{cases} 7x - y = 8 \\ -7x + y = 4 \end{cases}$$

**8.** _____

**9.** Find all solutions of the system.

$$\begin{cases} 3x - y = 2 \\ -3x + y = -2 \end{cases}$$

**9.** _____

**10.** *Annual Interest*   A total of $10,000 is invested in two funds paying 5% and 7% annual interest. The combined annual interest is $630. How much of the $10,000 is invested in each fund?

**10.** _____

**11.** *Salad Increments*   A salad contains $x$ pounds of ham and $y$ pounds of chicken. There are at most 6 pounds of ham and chicken in the salad. Write a system of inequalities to represent this situation. Sketch a graph of the system.

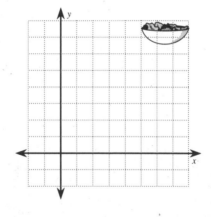

**11.** _____
   *Use graph at left.*

**12.** Sketch the graph of the system of linear inequalities.

$$\begin{cases} y < 2x + 1 \\ y > \tfrac{1}{2}x - 2 \end{cases}$$

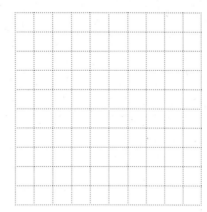

**12.** *Use graph at left.*

**13.** Sketch the graph of the constraints. Label the vertices of the graph.

$$\begin{cases} x + y \le 7 \\ \phantom{x + }y \le 6 \\ x \phantom{ + y}\le 5 \\ x \phantom{ + y}\ge 0 \\ \phantom{x + }y \ge 0 \end{cases}$$

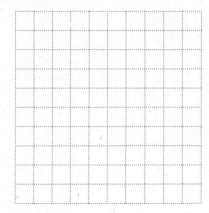

**13.** *Use graph at left.*

**14.** Find the *maximum* value of the objective quantity $C$.

$C = 2x - 7y$   Constraints:
$$\begin{cases} y \le 2x + 2 \\ x \le \phantom{2}3 \\ y \ge \phantom{2}0 \end{cases}$$

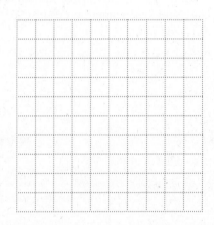

**14.** _____
*Use graph at left.*

**15.** **Maximum Profit**   A manufacturer produces $x$ widgets and $y$ gidgets that have profits of $8 and $4 each, respectively. Each product goes through two processes with the required times as shown in the table. Find the daily production level for each product so that the profit is a maximum.

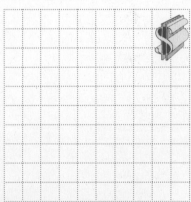

**15.** _____
*Use graph at left.*

| Process | Hours to Produce a Widget | Hours to Produce a Gidget | Hours Available per Day |
|---------|---------------------------|---------------------------|-------------------------|
| I | 1 | 2 | 10 |
| II | 2 | 1 | 8 |

   *Algebra 1*

In 1–3, describe whether the system graphically represents parallel lines, intersecting lines, or a single line. Also state whether the system has one solution, many solutions, or no solution.

1. $\begin{cases} 3x + \phantom{4}y = 4 \\ \phantom{3}x + 4y = 2 \end{cases}$

1. _____

2. $\begin{cases} \phantom{-}x - 3y = \phantom{-}7 \\ -x + 3y = -7 \end{cases}$

2. _____

3. $\begin{cases} y = -\frac{2}{3}x + 1 \\ y = -\frac{2}{3}x - 1 \end{cases}$

3. _____

In 4, use a straightedge to draw straight lines.

4. Solve the linear system by graphing.
$\begin{cases} y = \frac{2}{3}x + 2 \\ y = -x - 3 \end{cases}$

4. _____
*Use graph at left.*

5. Use substitution to solve the linear system.
$\begin{cases} \phantom{2}x - 4y = \phantom{-}6 \\ 2x + \phantom{4}y = -4 \end{cases}$

5. _____

6. Use linear combinations to solve the linear system.
$\begin{cases} 3x + 2y = -5 \\ 4x - 3y = \phantom{-}16 \end{cases}$

6. _____

7. Solve the linear system by any method.
$\begin{cases} 6x - 4y = -1 \\ 2x + 5y = \phantom{-}1 \end{cases}$

7. _____

**8.** Find the solution of the system, if it exists.

$$\begin{cases} 4x - 2y = \phantom{0}3 \\ 2x - \phantom{0}y = 10 \end{cases}$$

8. _____

**9.** Find all solutions of the system.

$$\begin{cases} \frac{1}{2}x - \frac{1}{4}y = 12 \\ \phantom{0}x - \frac{1}{2}y = 24 \end{cases}$$

9. _____

**10.** *Candy Mixture*   $x$ pounds of candy valued at $3.50 per pound is mixed with $y$ pounds of candy valued at $4.30 per pound to produce 10 pounds of a mixture selling for $4 per pound. Find $x$ and $y$, the number of pounds of each type.

10. _____

**11.** *Fuel Mixture*   Fuel $x$ costs $2 per gallon and Fuel $y$ costs $3 per gallon. You have at most $18 to spend on fuel. Write a system of linear inequalities to represent this situation. Sketch a graph of the system.

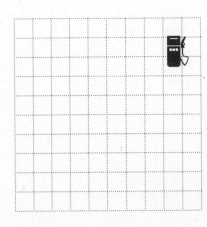

11. _____
*Use graph at left.*

**12.** Sketch the graph of the system of linear inequalities.

$$\begin{cases} y \geq \phantom{0}\frac{1}{3}x - 2 \\ y > -2x - 2 \end{cases}$$

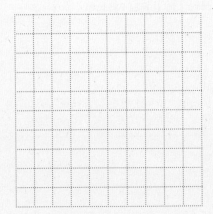

12. *Use graph at left.*

**13.** Sketch the graph of the constraints. Label the vertices of the graph.

$$\begin{cases} x \leq 6 \\ x \geq 0 \\ y \geq 0 \\ y \leq x + 3 \\ y \leq 6 \end{cases}$$

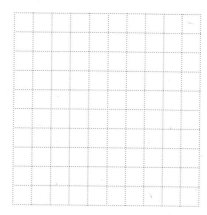

**13.** _Use graph at left._

**14.** Find the *maximum* value of the objective quantity $C$.

$C = 6x + 2y$    Constraints:

$$\begin{cases} y \leq 2x + 4 \\ y \leq -\frac{4}{5}x + 4 \\ y \geq 0 \end{cases}$$

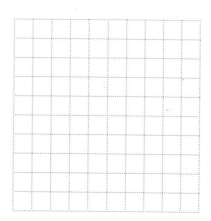

**14.** _____
_Use graph at left._

**15. Maximum Profit**    A manufacturer produces $x$ widgets and $y$ gidgets that have profits of \$4 and \$6 each, respectively. Each product goes through three processes with the required times as shown in the table. Find the daily production level for each product so that the profit is a maximum.

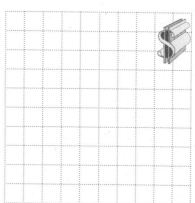

**15.** _____
_Use graph at left._

| Process | Hours to Produce a Widget | Hours to Produce a Gidget | Hours Available per Day |
|---------|---------------------------|---------------------------|-------------------------|
| I | 1 | 1 | 10 |
| II | 1 | 3 | 24 |
| III | 3 | 2 | 27 |

1. Simplify $(-3xy^2)^2(x^2y)^3$.

1. _____

2. Which is larger, $3^4$ or $5^3$?

2. _____

3. Solve the equation for $x$.
$$(2^3)^4 = 2^x$$

3. _____

4. Rewrite the expression using positive exponents.
$$\frac{6x^{-2}}{5y^{-3}}$$

4. _____

5. Evaluate the expression $5^{-6} \cdot 5^8$.

5. _____

6. Evaluate $2 \cdot 4^0$.

6. _____

7. Evaluate the expression $\dfrac{2^3 \cdot 2^{-5}}{2^{-2}}$.

7. _____

8. **Radioactive Decay**    The half-life of carbon-14 is 5700 years. If you start with 10 grams of carbon-14, how much will remain in 22,800 years?

8. _____

9. Evaluate and write the answer in both decimal and scientific notation.
$$(3 \times 10^{-7})(7 \times 10^5)$$

9. _____

10. **Distance to a Star**    A light-year is approximately $5.88 \times 10^{12}$ miles. Estimate the distance from Earth to a star so far away that its light takes 9.4 years to reach us.

10. _____

1. Simplify $(-2A^2B)^3(AB^2)^2$.

1. _____

2. Which is larger, $3^5$ or $5^4$?

2. _____

3. Solve the equation for $x$.
   $$(3^5)^3 = 3^x$$

3. _____

4. Rewrite the expression using positive exponents.
   $$(-3x)^{-3}$$

4. _____

5. Evaluate the expression $4^{-15} \cdot 4^{16}$.

5. _____

6. Evaluate $-3 \cdot 3^0$.

6. _____

7. Evaluate the expression $\dfrac{2^5 \cdot 2^{-3}}{2^6}$.

7. _____

8. **Radioactive Decay**   The half-life of carbon-14 is 5700 years. If you start with 20 grams of carbon-14, how much will remain in 17,100 years?

8. _____

9. Evaluate and write the answer in both decimal and scientific notation.
   $$(9 \times 10^{-5})(4 \times 10^7)$$

9. _____

10. **Distance to a Star**   A light-year is approximately $5.88 \times 10^{12}$ miles. Estimate the distance from Earth to a star so far away that its light takes 15.3 years to reach us.

10. _____

1. Simplify, $(8x^3)^2(\frac{1}{4}x^2)^3$.

1. _____

2. Evaluate $(a^3b^2)^2$ when $a = -1$ and $b = -2$.

2. _____

3. Solve for $x$.
$$2^3 \cdot 2^4 = 2^x$$

3. _____

4. Rewrite the expression using positive exponents.
$$\frac{1}{9x^{-2}y^{-1}}$$

4. _____

5. Evaluate $-5 \cdot 4^0$.

5. _____

6. Rewrite the expression using positive exponents.
$$(-3)^0(2x^{-1}y^{-1})^2$$

6. _____

7. Evaluate the expression $\dfrac{7^4}{7^5}$.

7. _____

8. Simplify the expression
$$\frac{32xy^3}{-8x^3y} \cdot \frac{-2xy}{-4y}.$$

8. _____

9. Rewrite $2.13 \times 10^{-8}$ in decimal form.

9. _____

10. Rewrite 50,800,000 in scientific notation.

10. _____

11. Evaluate $(7 \times 10^7) \cdot (5 \times 10^{-6})$ without a calculator. Write the result in *decimal* form.

11. _____

12. Evaluate $(2.71 \times 10^{-3})^2$ and write the result in both decimal form and scientific notation.

12. _____

13. **Mass of a Proton**    The mass of a proton is $1.67 \times 10^{-24}$ gram. How many protons would weigh one gram?

13. _____

14. **Speed of Light**    Earth is approximately $9.3 \times 10^7$ miles from the sun. Light travels at approximately $1.87 \times 10^5$ miles per second. How long does it take light to travel from the sun to Earth?

14. _____

15. **Geometry**    The side of a cube is $7.24 \times 10^2$ inches. Write the *volume* of the cube in scientific notation.

15. _____

**16.** ***Balance in an Account***     A principal of $500 is deposited in an account that pays 6% annual interest compounded yearly. Find the balance after 10 years.

16. _____

**17.** ***Deposit in an Account***     How much must you deposit in an account that pays 7% annual interest compounded yearly to have a balance of $500 after 5 years?

17. _____

**18.** Choose the equation that represents *exponential decay*.

    **a.** $y = (0.89)^t$    **b.** $y = (2.16)^t$

18. _____

**19.** ***School Enrollment***     The enrollment at Alpha-Beta School District has been declining 3% each year from 1986 to 1992. If the enrollment in 1986 was 2583, find the 1992 enrollment.

19. _____
    *Use graph at left.*

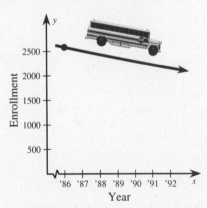

**1.** Simplify $(2x)^4 \left(\frac{1}{2}x^3\right)^2$.

1. _____

**2.** Evaluate $(A^7 B^2)^3$ when $A = 1$ and $B = -2$.

2. _____

**3.** Solve for $x$.
$$3^2 \cdot 3^4 \cdot 3^5 = 3^x$$

3. _____

**4.** Rewrite the expression using positive exponents.
$$5AB^{-2}$$

4. _____

**5.** Evaluate $-3 \cdot (-2)^x$ when $x = 4$.

5. _____

**6.** Rewrite the expression using positive exponents.
$$\frac{-3^0}{4x^{-3}}$$

6. _____

**7.** Evaluate the expression $\dfrac{5^4 \cdot 5^5}{5^6}$.

7. _____

**8.** Simplify the expression
$$\frac{5x^3 y^{-1}}{x^{-2} y^2} \cdot \frac{(5x^2 y)^{-1}}{x y^{-1}}.$$

8. _____

**9.** Rewrite $3.94 \times 10^9$ in decimal form.

9. _____

**10.** Rewrite $0.00000428$ in scientific notation.

10. _____

**11.** Evaluate $(7 \times 10^{-3}) \bullet (4 \times 10^5)$ without a calculator. Write the result in *decimal* form.

11. _____

**12.** Evaluate $(6.19 \times 10^{-2})^2$ and write the result in both decimal form and scientific notation.

12. _____

**13.** *Mass of a Proton*   The mass of a proton is $1.67 \times 10^{-27}$ kilogram. How many protons would weigh one kilogram?

13. _____

**14.** *Speed of Light*   Light travels approximately $5.88 \times 10^{12}$ miles per year. If the light from a certain star takes 112 years to reach Earth, find the distance to the star in *miles*.

14. _____

**15.** *Geometry*   The side of a square is $3.84 \times 10^{-3}$ inches. Write the *area* of the square in scientific notation.

15. _____

   *Algebra 1*

16. ***Balance in an Account***    A principal of $500 is deposited in an account that pays 7% annual interest compounded yearly. Find the balance after 10 years.

16. _____

17. ***Deposit in an Account***    How much must you deposit in an account that pays 6% annual interest compounded yearly to have a balance of $500 after 5 years?

17. _____

18. Choose the equation that represents *exponential decay*.

    **a.**  $y = (1.081)^t$    **b.**  $y = (0.79)^t$

18. _____

19. ***School Enrollment***    The enrollment at Alpha-Gamma School District has been declining 4% each year from 1986 to 1992. If the enrollment in 1986 was 1575, find the 1992 enrollment.

19. _____
    *Use graph at left.*

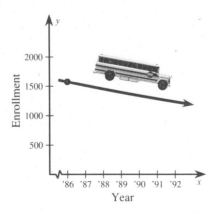

A  **1.** Simplify  $(-x)^2(-x^2)^2(-x^3)$.

1. _____

B  **2.** Evaluate $(a^3b^2)^3$ when $a = -1$ and $b = -2$.

2. _____

C  **3.** Solve for $x$.
$$3^3 \cdot 3^x \cdot 3^5 = 3^{15}$$

3. _____

**4.** Rewrite the expression using positive exponents.
$$\frac{7A^{-1}}{B^{-2}}$$

4. _____

**5.** Evaluate $[-3(-2)^x]^{-1}$ when $x = 2$.

5. _____

**6.** Rewrite the expression using positive exponents.
$$(-2)^0(3x^{-2}y^{-2})^{-1}$$

6. _____

D  **7.** Evaluate the expression $\dfrac{5^{-4} \cdot 5^{-5}}{5^{-6}}$.

7. _____

E  **8.** Simplify the expression
$$\frac{8x^2y^{-2}}{x^{-2}y} \cdot \frac{(4xy^2)^{-1}}{x^2y}.$$

8. _____

F)

G)

F **9.** Rewrite $3.15 \times 10^{-8}$ in decimal form.

9. _____

G **10.** Rewrite $0.0000000000193$ in scientific notation.

10. _____

**11.** Evaluate $(8.3 \times 10^{-5})(2 \times 10^{12})$ without a calculator. Write the result in *decimal* form.

11. _____

**12.** Evaluate $(1.87 \times 10^{-3})^{-2}$.

12. _____

**13.** *Mass of an Electron*    The mass of an electron is $9.11 \times 10^{-28}$ gram. How many electrons would weigh one gram?

13. _____

**14.** *Distance to a Star*    Light travels approximately $5.88 \times 10^{12}$ miles per year. A certain star is $109,000,000,000,000$ miles from Earth. Express this distance in *light years*.

14. _____

**15.** *Geometry*    The volume of a sphere is $\frac{4}{3}\pi r^3$ where $r$ is the radius and $\pi \approx 3.14$. If the radius of a certain sphere is 17.2 feet, write its *volume* in scientific notation.

15. _____

16. **Balance in an Account**  A principal of $500 is deposited in an account that pays 6.5% annual interest compounded yearly. Find the balance after 10 years.

16. _____

17. **Deposit in an Account**  How much must you deposit in an account that pays 7.5% annual interest compounded yearly to have a balance of $500 after 5 years?

17. _____

18. Choose the equation that represents *exponential decay*.

    **a.** $y = (1.06)^t$  **b.** $y = (0.94)^t$

18. _____

19. **School Enrollment**  The enrollment at Beta-Gamma School District has been declining 3.5% each year from 1986 to 1992. If the enrollment in 1986 was 1815, find the 1992 enrollment.

19. _____
    *Use graph at left.*

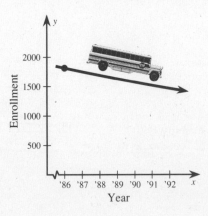

© D. C. Heath and Company  *Algebra 1*

Name _____

Date _____

**1.** Find all square roots of the number $\frac{36}{49}$.

1. _____

**2.** Evaluate $-\sqrt{196}$. Give the exact value, if possible. Otherwise, give an approximation to two decimal places.

2. _____

**3. *Geometry***  Find the hypotenuse of the triangle. Round your result to one decimal place.

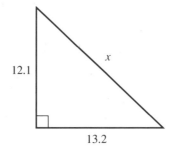

3. _____

**4. *Geometry***  The radius of a circle is given by $r = \sqrt{\dfrac{A}{\pi}}$, where $A$ is the area and $\pi \approx 3.14$. Find the radius, to two decimal places, of a circle whose area is 216 square inches.

4. _____

**5.** Solve the equation $3A^2 - 92 = 100$.

5. _____

**6. *Falling Object***  An object is dropped from an initial height of $s$ feet. The object's height at any time $t$, in seconds, is given by $h = -16t^2 + s$. How long does it take an object dropped from 400 feet to reach the ground?

6. _____

**7.** Find the vertex of $y = -x^2 - 2x - 3$.

7. _____

**8.** Sketch the graph of $y = -x^2 + 4x$. Label the vertex and $x$-intercepts.

8.  *Use graph at left.*

**9.** Solve $x^2 + 2x - 15 = 0$.

9. _____

**10.** Use the quadratic formula to solve the equation $3x^2 + x - 10 = 0$.

10. _____

Name _____

Date _____

1. Find all square roots of the number $\frac{81}{16}$.

1. _____

2. Evaluate $\sqrt{0.81}$. Give the exact value, if possible. Otherwise, give an approximation to two decimal places.

2. _____

3. **Geometry**  Find the hypotenuse of the triangle. Round your result to one decimal place.

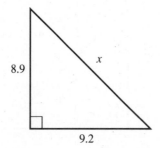

8.9

$x$

9.2

3. _____

4. **Geometry**  The radius of a circle is given by $r = \sqrt{\dfrac{A}{\pi}}$, where $A$ is the area and $\pi \approx 3.14$. Find the radius, to two decimal places, of a circle whose area is 347 square inches.

4. _____

5. Solve the equation $2A^2 - 2 = 70$.

5. _____

6. **Falling Object**  An object is dropped from an initial height of $s$ feet. The object's height at any time $t$, in seconds, is given by $h = -16t^2 + s$. How long does it take an object dropped from 225 feet to reach the ground?

6. _____

7. Find the vertex of $y = -x^2 - 4x - 1$.

7. _____

8. Sketch the graph of $y = -x^2 + 2x + 3$. Label the vertex and $x$-intercepts.

8. _Use graph at left._

9. Solve $x^2 - 3x - 18 = 0$.

9. _____

10. Use the quadratic formula to solve the equation $4x^2 + 9x - 9 = 0$.

10. _____

1. Find all square roots of the number 0.25.

1. _____

**In 2–4, evaluate the expression. Give the exact value, if possible; otherwise, approximate to two decimal places.**

2. $-\sqrt{\frac{121}{64}}$

2. _____

3. $\sqrt{29}$

3. _____

4. $\dfrac{15 - 2\sqrt{7}}{3}$

4. _____

5. Solve the equation $\frac{1}{6}x^2 = 54$.

6. Solve the equation. Round yo...
   $5x^2 = 75$

7. **Geometry** Find the hypo...
   of the triangle. Round your
   result to two decimal place...

7. _____

8. **Falling Object** An object is dropped from an initial height of
   $s$ feet. The object's height at any time $t$, in seconds, is given by
   $h = -16t^2 + s$. How long does it take for an object dropped from
   200 feet to hit the ground? Round your result to two decimal places.

8. _____

9. Find the coordinates of the vertex and determine whether the graph opens *up* or *down*.

$$y = -x^2 + 5$$

9. _____

10. *Tossing a Ball*    You toss a ball that travels on the path

$$y = -0.1x^2 + x + 2$$

where $x$ and $y$ are measured in meters. Sketch the path of the ball. How high does the ball go?

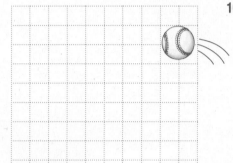

10. _____
    *Use graph at left.*

**In 11 and 12, use the quadratic formula to solve the equation to the exact value or round to two decimal places.**

11. $x^2 - x = 2$

11. _____

12. $x^2 - x - 3 = 0$

12. _____

13. Decide how many solutions the equation has.

$$x^2 - 4x + 4 = 0$$

13. _____

14. *Falling Object*    The height of an object thrown upward with velocity $v$ feet per second is given by $h = -16t^2 + vt$, where $t$ is time measured in seconds. If an object is thrown upward with a velocity of 80 ft/sec from ground level, ($h = 0$), how long will it take to return to ground level?

14. _____

**In 15 and 16, decide whether the point is a solution of the inequality.**

**15.** $y \geq 2x^2 - 5x - 7$, $(-2, 10)$

**15.** _____

**16.** $y \leq -3x^2 + 2x + 30$, $(-3, -4)$

**16.** _____

**In 17 and 18, sketch the graph of the inequality.**

**17.** $y \leq x^2 - 2x - 3$

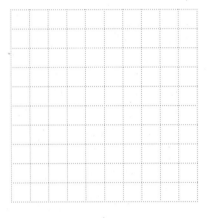

**17.** *Use graph at left.*

**18.** $y < -x^2 + 4$

**18.** *Use graph at left.*

1. Find all square roots of the number 0.64.

1. _____

**In 2–4, evaluate the expression. Give the exact value, if possible; otherwise, approximate to two decimal places.**

2. $-\sqrt{\frac{81}{121}}$

2. _____

3. $\sqrt{39}$

3. _____

4. $\dfrac{6 - 3\sqrt{7}}{4}$

4. _____

5. Solve the equation $\frac{1}{3}x^2 = 48$.

5. _____

6. Solve the equation. Round your results to two decimal places.

$$6x^2 = 961$$

6. _____

7. **Geometry** Find the hypotenuse of the triangle. Round your result to one decimal place.

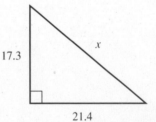

7. _____

8. **Falling Object** An object is dropped from an initial height of $s$ feet. The object's height at any time $t$, in seconds, is given by $h = -16t^2 + s$. How long does it take for an object dropped from 300 feet to hit the ground? Round your result to two decimal places.

8. _____

9. Find the coordinates of the vertex and determine whether the graph opens *up* or *down*.

$$y = x^2 - 5$$

9. _____

10. ***Tossing a Ball***    You toss a ball that travels on the path

$$y = -0.1x^2 + x + 3$$

where $x$ and $y$ are measured in meters. Sketch the path of the ball. How high does the ball go?

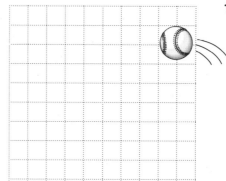

10. _____
*Use graph at left.*

**In 11 and 12, use the quadratic formula to solve the equation to the exact value or round to two decimal places.**

11. $x^2 - x = 6$

11. _____

12. $x^2 - x - 5 = 0$

12. _____

13. Decide how many solutions the equation has.

$$x^2 - 6x + 8 = 0$$

13. _____

14. ***Falling Object***    The height of an object thrown upward with velocity $v$ feet per second is given by $h = -16t^2 + vt$, where $t$ is time measured in seconds. If an object is thrown upward with a velocity of 96 ft/sec from ground level, $(h = 0)$, how long will it take to return to ground level?

14. _____

**In 15 and 16, decide whether the point is a solution of the inequality.**

**15.** $y \geq -2x^2 + 5x + 7,\ (-2,\ 10)$

**15.** _____

**16.** $y \leq 3x^2 - 2x - 30,\ (-3,\ 4)$

**16.** _____

**In Problems 17 and 18, sketch the graph of the inequality.**

**17.** $y > x^2 - 2x - 3$

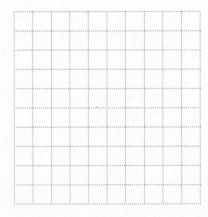

**17.** *Use graph at left.*

**18.** $y \geq -x^2 + 4$

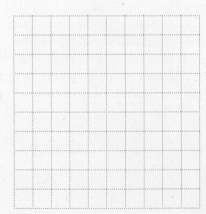

**18.** *Use graph at left.*

**Form C**

(Page 1 of 3 pages)

Name _____

Date _____

1. Find all square roots of the number 0.0081.

1. _____

**In 2–4, evaluate the expression. Give the exact value, if possible; otherwise, approximate to two decimal places.**

2. $-\sqrt{\dfrac{900}{169}}$

2. _____

3. $\sqrt{72.4}$

3. _____

4. $\dfrac{1 - 5\sqrt{17}}{2}$

4. _____

5. Solve the equation $\frac{1}{12}x^2 = 75$.

5. _____

6. Solve the equation. Round your results to two decimal places.
   $$7x^2 - 4 = 100$$

6. _____

7. **Geometry**   Find the side of the triangle. Round your result to one decimal place.

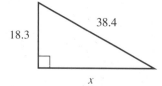

7. _____

8. **Falling Object**   An object is dropped from an initial height of $s$ feet. The object's height at any time $t$, in seconds, is given by $h = -16t^2 + s$. How long does it take for an object dropped from 254 feet to hit the ground? Round your result to two decimal places.

8. _____

9. Find the coordinates of the vertex and determine whether the graph opens *up* or *down*.

$$y = -x^2 + x - 5$$

9. _____

10. **Tossing a Ball**    You toss a ball that travels on the path
$$y = -0.1x^2 + x + 1.5$$
where $x$ and $y$ are measured in meters. Sketch the path of the ball. How high does the ball go?

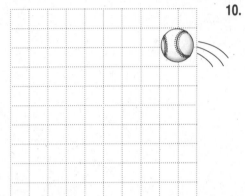

10. _____
*Use graph at left.*

**In 11 and 12, use the quadratic formula to solve the equation to the exact value or round to two decimal places.**

11. $2x^2 - x = 1$

11. _____

12. $3x^2 - x - 3 = 0$

12. _____

13. Decide how many solutions the equation has.
$$x^2 + x + 1 = 0$$

13. _____

14. **Falling Object**    The height of an object thrown upward with velocity $v$ feet per second is given by $h = -16t^2 + vt$, where $t$ is time measured in seconds. If an object is thrown upward with a velocity of 100 ft/sec from ground level, $(h = 0)$, how long will it take to return to ground level?

14. _____

**In 15 and 16, decide whether the point is a solution of the inequality.**

**15.** $y \leq 2x^2 - 5x - 7$, $(3, -4)$

15. _____

**16.** $y > -3x^2 + 2x + 40$, $(4, 0)$

16. _____

**In 17 and 18, sketch the graph of the inequality.**

**17.** $y \leq -x^2 - x + 2$

17. _Use graph at left._

**18.** $y > 2x^2 - 4x - 4$

18. _Use graph at left._

**Use a straightedge to draw straight lines.**

1. State whether the system represents parallel lines, intersecting lines, or a single line. Also state whether there is one, none, or many solutions.

$$\begin{cases} 5x - 7y = 4 \\ 10x - 14y = 1 \end{cases}$$

1. _____

2. Solve the linear system by graphing.

$$\begin{cases} x - 3y = 3 \\ x + y = -1 \end{cases}$$

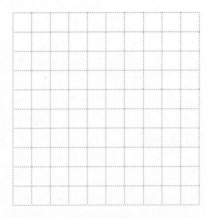

2. *Use graph at left.*

3. Use substitution to solve the linear system.

$$\begin{cases} x + 2y = 6 \\ 2x - y = 7 \end{cases}$$

3. _____

4. Use linear combinations to solve the linear system.

$$\begin{cases} 5x + 2y = 8 \\ 2x - 5y = 9 \end{cases}$$

4. _____

5. Solve the linear system by any method.

$$\begin{cases} 3x - y = -2 \\ 6x + 2y = 12 \end{cases}$$

5. _____

6. Find all solutions to the system.

$$\begin{cases} 2x - 6y = -1 \\ -4x + 12y = 2 \end{cases}$$

6. _____

7. **Annual Interest**   A total of $15,000 is invested in two funds paying 6% and 8% annual interest. The combined interest is $1090. How much of the $15,000 is invested in each fund?

7. _____

8. Sketch the graph of the system of linear inequalities.

$$\begin{cases} x \geq -3 \\ y \leq \phantom{-}2 \end{cases}$$

8. *Use graph at left.*

9. Sketch the graph of the system of linear inequalities.

$$\begin{cases} y > -x + 5 \\ y > \frac{1}{3}x + 1 \end{cases}$$

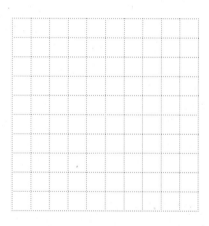

9. *Use graph at left.*

10. Sketch the graph of the constraints. Label the vertices of the graph.

$$\begin{cases} x \leq \phantom{-x+}4 \\ y \leq \phantom{-x+}3 \\ y \geq -x + 2 \end{cases}$$

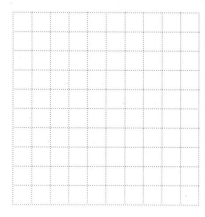

10. *Use graph at left.*

**11.** Find the *maximum and minimum* values of the objective quantity $C$.

$C = 3x - 6y$     Constraints
$$\begin{cases} x \leq \phantom{-}4 \\ x \geq -1 \\ y \leq -x + 6 \\ y \geq \phantom{-}0 \end{cases}$$

**11.** _____
*Use graph at left.*

**12.** Simplify $(3x^2)^5 \left(\dfrac{x^3}{9}\right)^2$, if possible.

**12.** _____

**13.** Evaluate $(A^2B^3)^3$ when $A = 2$ and $B = -1$.

**13.** _____

**14.** Rewrite the expression using positive exponents.

$$\dfrac{5^0 x^{-3}}{(y^{-2})^2}$$

**14.** _____

**15.** Solve for $x$.   $3^4 \cdot 3^3 \cdot (3^2)^2 = 3^x$

**15.** _____

**16.** Evaluate the expression $\dfrac{9^2 \cdot 3^5}{27^3}$.

**16.** _____

**17.** Simplify the expression $\dfrac{16a^2b^4}{-4b^3} \cdot \dfrac{-4a^5b}{-8a^3b^2}$.

17. _____

**18.** Rewrite in decimal form $7.81 \times 10^{-5}$.

18. _____

**19.** Rewrite in scientific notation 788,000,000,000.

19. _____

**20.** Evaluate without a calculator $(4 \times 10^8)(8 \times 10^{-6})$. Write the result in *decimal* form.

20. _____

**21.** Evaluate $(6.97 \times 10^{-5})^3$ and write the result in scientific notation.

21. _____

**22. Hydrogen Atom**    The mass of a hydrogen atom is $3.68 \times 10^{-27}$ pound. How many hydrogen atoms would weigh one pound?

22. _____

**23. Speed of Light**    Light travels at $1.87 \times 10^5$ miles per second. When Mars is 40,000,000 miles from Earth, how long does it take sunlight reflected from Mars to reach Earth?

23. _____

**24. Geometry**   The side of a cube is $6.18 \times 10^2$ meters. Write the volume of the cube in scientific notation.

24. _____

**25. Balance in an Account**   A principal of $700 is deposited in an account that pays 5.5% annual interest compounded yearly. Find the balance after 8 years.

25. _____

**26. Deposit in an Account**   How much must you deposit in an account which pays 7% annual interest compounded yearly to have a balance of $500 after 10 years?

26. _____

**27.** Choose the equation that represents *exponential decay*.
  **a.** $y = (1.87)^t$   **b.** $y = (0.871)^t$

27. _____

**28. School Enrollment**   The enrollment at Delta-Gamma School District has been declining 4.5% each year from 1985 to 1992. If the enrollment in 1985 was 3312, find the 1992 enrollment.

28. _____

**29.** Find all square roots of the number 0.09.    29. _____

**30.** Evaluate the expression $\dfrac{18 - 5\sqrt{3}}{4}$. Round to two decimal places.    30. _____

**31.** Solve the equation $\dfrac{x^2}{5} = 125$.    31. _____

**32.** Solve the equation. Round your results to two decimal places.
$$7x^2 = 89$$    32. _____

**33.** *Geometry*    Find the hypotenuse of the triangle to two decimal places.    33. _____

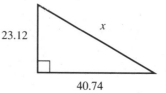

23.12

$x$

40.74

**34. *Falling Object***   $h = -16t^2 + s$ gives the height of an object, after $t$ seconds, which is dropped from a height of $s$ feet. How long does it take an object dropped from 500 feet to reach the ground? Round to two decimal places.

34. _____

**35.** Find the coordinates of the vertex. Does the graph open *up or down*?
$$y = 10 - 2x^2$$

35. _____

**36.** Sketch the graph of the equation. Label the vertex.
$$y = -x^2 - 2x + 2$$

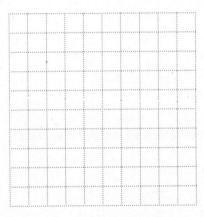

36.   *Use graph at left.*

**37.** Decide how many solutions the equation has.
$$4x^2 + 4x + 1 = 0$$

37. _____

**38.** Use the quadratic formula to solve the equation.
$$2x^2 - x - 3 = 0$$

38. _____

                    *Algebra 1*

**39.** Use the quadratic formula to solve the equation. Round to two decimal places.
$$x^2 + x - 4 = 0$$

39. _____

**In 40 and 41, decide whether the point is a solution of the inequality.**

**40.** $y \leq 3x^2 - 7x - 3$, $(3, 2)$

40. _____

**41.** $y > -2x^2 + 9$, $(2, 1)$

41. _____

**In 42 and 43, sketch the graph of the inequality.**

**42.** $y \leq x^2 - x - 6$

42.  *Use graph at left.*

**43.** $y > x^2 - 1$

43.  *Use graph at left.*

Name _____

Date _____

1. Add the polynomials
   $7x^3 - 3x^2 - 4x + 2$  and  $9x^3 + 7x^2 - 3x - 5$.

1. _____

2. Subtract $2z^3 - 7z + 4$ from $4z^3 + z^2 - 2z + 1$.

2. _____

3. Perform the indicated operations.
   $(2x^2 - x) - (2x^2 + 3x) + (3x^2 - 5x)$

3. _____

4. Multiply  $5x^2(3x - 2)$.

4. _____

5. Use the FOIL pattern to multiply $(2x + 1)(x - 3)$.

5. _____

6. **Geometry**    A rectangle is 8 meters long and 6 meters wide. It is enlarged by increasing each side by $x$ meters. Write the area of the larger rectangle in terms of a trinomial in $x$.

6. _____

7. Multiply  $(3x + 2)(3x - 2)$.

7. _____

8. Write $(2x - 4)^2$ as a trinomial.

8. _____

9. Find the greatest common factor of the three terms.
   $20x^3y^2$,  $16x^4y$,  $24x^2y^3$

9. _____

10. Factor the expression  $32x^2 - 98y^2$.

10. _____

1. Add the polynomials
$6x^3 + 2x^2 - 3x - 2$ and $-2x^3 + 3x^2 + 4x + 5$.

1. _____

2. Subtract $3z^3 + z^2 - 5$ from $5z^3 - 3z + 7$.

2. _____

3. Perform the indicated operations.
$(3x^2 - 2x) - (2x^2 + x) + (x^2 - 4x)$

3. _____

4. Multiply $8x^2(4x - 2)$.

4. _____

5. Use the FOIL pattern to multiply $(5x - 2)(2x + 3)$.

5. _____

6. **Geometry** A rectangle is 5 meters long and 4 meters wide. It is enlarged by increasing each side by $x$ meters. Write the area of the larger rectangle in terms of a trinomial in $x$.

6. _____

7. Multiply $(2x - 4)(2x + 4)$.

7. _____

8. Write $(2x - 5)^2$ as a trinomial.

8. _____

9. Find the greatest common factor of the three terms.
$15x^4y^3$, $25x^3y^4$, $10x^2y^5$

9. _____

10. Factor the expression $12x^2 - 12x + 3$.

10. _____

1. Add the polynomials $3x^2 - 5x + 7$ and $4x^2 + 8x - 3$.

1. _____

2. Subtract $x^3 - 2x^2 + 4$ from $3x^3 - 7x - 5$.

2. _____

3. Perform the indicated operations.
   $$-3(4u + 2) + 5(2u - 3) - 3(3u - 4)$$

3. _____

4. Multiply $-x^2(-3x^2 + 2x - 4)$.

4. _____

5. Use the FOIL pattern to multiply $(x - 3)(3x + 5)$.

5. _____

6. Write $(3x - 2)^2$ as a trinomial.

6. _____

7. Multiply $(7x - 4)(7x + 4)$.

7. _____

8. Find the greatest common factor of the three terms.
   $12A^4B^3, \ 36A^3B^5, \ 54A^4B^4$

8. _____

9. Factor out the greatest common monomial factor.
$21z^3 + 28z$

9. _____

10. Factor the expression $y^2 - 256$.

10. _____

11. Factor the expression $4x^2 + 28xy + 49y^2$.

11. _____

12. Factor the expression $3x^2 + 24x + 48$.

12. _____

13. **Geometry**    The area of a circle is given by $A = \pi(9x^2 + 12x + 4)$. Find an expression for the *radius* of the circle.

13. _____

14. **Width of Pond**    The bed of a pond can be modeled by $30y = x^2 - 14x + 13$, where $x$ and $y$ are measured in meters and the $x$-axis matches the water level of the pond. What is the width of the pond?

14. _____

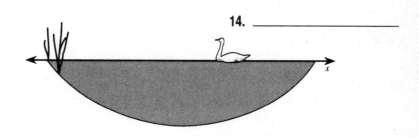

**15.** Solve the equation $(x + 3)(x - 7) = 0$.

15. _____

**16.** Solve the equation $2x^2 + 3x - 9 = 0$.

16. _____

**17.** Solve the equation $5x^2 + 2x = 0$.

17. _____

**18.** Find the term that must be added to the expression to create a perfect square trinomial.

$$x^2 + 18x$$

18. _____

**19.** Solve by completing the square.

$$t^2 + 6t - 3 = 0$$

19. _____

**20. _Swimming Pool_**    The length of a rectangular swimming pool is 30 feet longer than the width. If it covers an area of 4000 square feet, find the length and width.

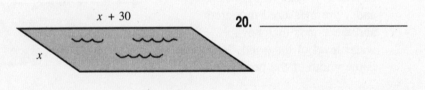

$x + 30$

$x$

20. _____

**Chapter 10 Test** **Form B**
*(Page 1 of 3 pages)*

Name _____

Date _____

1. Add the polynomials $2x^2 - 7x + 7$ and $-3x^2 - 2x + 8$.

   1. _____

2. Subtract $z^3 - 3z - 6$ from $3z^3 + 2z^2 + 7$.

   2. _____

3. Perform the indicated operations.
   $$-2(y - 4) - 3(2y + 3) + 4(y - 1)$$

   3. _____

4. Multiply $-3x^2(2x^2 - 5x - 3)$.

   4. _____

5. Use the FOIL pattern to multiply $(2x - 5)(3x + 4)$.

   5. _____

6. Write $(4x - 3)^2$ as a trinomial.

   6. _____

7. Multiply $(8x - 3)(8x + 3)$.

   7. _____

8. Find the greatest common factor of the three terms.
   $$15A^5B^4, \ 21A^3B^3, \ 27A^2B^5$$

   8. _____

**9.** Factor out the greatest common monomial factor.
$24u^3 + 40u^2$

9. _____

**10.** Factor the expression $z^2 - 81$.

10. _____

**11.** Factor the expression $9x^2 - 30xy + 25y^2$.

11. _____

**12.** Factor the expression $4m^2 + 40m + 100$.

12. _____

**13.** *Geometry*    The area of a circle is given by
$A = \pi(25x^2 + 10x + 1)$. Find an expression for the *radius* of the
circle.

13. _____

**14.** *Width of Pond*    The bed of a
pond can be modeled by
$30y = x^2 - 15x + 14$, where $x$
and $y$ are measured in meters
and the $x$-axis matches the
water level of the pond. What
is the width of the pond?

14. _____

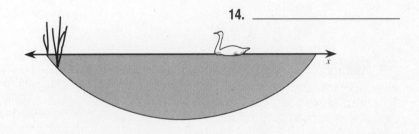

**15.** Solve the equation $(x + 4)(x + 2) = 0$.

15. _____

**16.** Solve the equation $4x^2 + 7x - 2 = 0$.

16. _____

**17.** Solve the equation $7x^2 + 3x = 0$.

17. _____

**18.** Find the term that must be added to the expression to create a perfect square trinomial.

$$x^2 + 22x$$

18. _____

**19.** Solve by completing the square.

$$r^2 - 4r - 7 = 0$$

19. _____

**20.** ***Swimming Pool***    The length of a rectangular swimming pool is 30 feet longer than the width. If it covers an area of 2800 square feet, find the length and width.

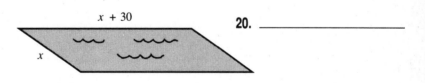

20. _____

**1.** Add the polynomials $-5x^2 + 7x - 2$ and $2 - 3x + 4x^2$.

1. _____

**2.** Subtract $-z^3 - 2z + 4$ from $z^3 + 4z^2 + 5z$.

2. _____

**3.** Perform the indicated operations.
$$A(3 - 2A) + 5(4 + 2A) - 3(2 - A^2)$$

3. _____

**4.** Multiply $-z^2(3 - z - 2z^2)$.

4. _____

**5.** Use the FOIL pattern to multiply $(a^2 + 2)(3a - 1)$.

5. _____

**6.** Write $(x^2 - 4)^2$ as a trinomial.

6. _____

**7.** Multiply $(5z^2 - 3)(5z^2 + 3)$.

7. _____

**8.** Find the greatest common factor of the three terms.
$$48A^{10}y^7, \; 64A^8y^6, \; 72A^9y^7$$

8. _____

9. Factor out the greatest common monomial factor.
   $18u^4v^5 + 30u^5v^4$

   9. _____

10. Factor the expression $81z^2 - 121$.

    10. _____

11. Factor the expression $16x^4 + 40x^2y^2 + 25y^4$.

    11. _____

12. Factor the expression $5m^4 - 70m^3 + 245m^2$.

    12. _____

13. **Geometry**    The area of a circle is given by
    $A = \pi(x^4 + 2x^2 + 1)$.
    Find an expression for the *radius* of the circle.

    13. _____

14. **Width of Pond**    The bed of
    a pond can be modeled by
    $30y = 2x^2 - 25x + 12$, where $x$
    and $y$ are measured in meters
    and the $x$-axis matches the
    water level of the pond. What
    is the width of the pond?

    14. _____

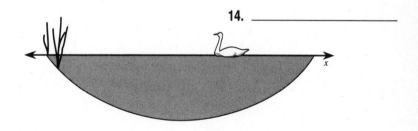

**15.** Solve the equation $(2x - 3)(3x + 2) = 0$.          15. _____

**16.** Solve the equation $30x^2 + 11x - 30 = 0$.          16. _____

**17.** Solve the equation $3x - 7x^2 = 0$.          17. _____

**18.** Find the term that must be added to the expression to create a perfect          18. _____
square trinomial.
$$x^2 + 15x$$

**19.** Solve by completing the square.          19. _____
$$w^2 + 5w + 2 = 0$$

**20.** **Swimming Pool**   The length
of a rectangular swimming
pool is 10 feet less than twice
its width. Find its length and
width if its area is 4500 square
feet.

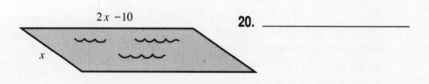

20. _____

1. Solve the proportion $\dfrac{5}{x} = \dfrac{7}{2}$.

   1. _____

2. Solve the proportion $\dfrac{x+4}{4} = \dfrac{x}{x-2}$.

   2. _____

**In 3–5, use your calculator. Give answers to one decimal place where needed.**

3. What is 15% of 700 meters?

   3. _____

4. 25.6 is what percent of 186?

   4. _____

5. 35 is 2.5% of what number?

   5. _____

6. $x$ and $y$ vary *directly*. If $x = 7$ when $y = 28$, write the equation that relates the variables.

   6. _____

7. **Gas Law**    The volume, $V$, of a gas varies *inversely* as the pressure, $P$. When the volume is 450 cubic centimeters, the pressure is 3.2 atmospheres. Write an equation relating $V$ and $P$.

   7. _____

8. Find the probability of an event occurring if there are 3 successful ways in 20 possibilities.

   8. _____

9. What is the probability of an event that cannot occur?

   9. _____

10. **Committee Choice**    You are one of a group of 3 people on a committee. One person is chosen at random to chair the committee. What is the probability that you are chosen?

    10. _____

**1.** Solve the proportion $\dfrac{6}{x-2} = \dfrac{2}{3}$.

1. _____

**2.** Solve the proportion $\dfrac{x}{x+6} = \dfrac{1}{x}$.

2. _____

**In 3–5, use your calculator. Give answers to one decimal place where needed.**

**3.** What is 24% of 850 pounds?

3. _____

**4.** 46.6 is what percent of 295?

4. _____

**5.** 155 is 12.5% of what number?

5. _____

**6.** $x$ and $y$ vary *directly*. If $x = 28$ when $y = 21$, write the equation that relates the variables.

6. _____

**7.** *Gas Law*    The volume, $V$, of a gas varies *inversely* as the pressure, $P$. When the volume is 10.5 liters, the pressure is 2 atmospheres. Write an equation relating $V$ and $P$.

7. _____

**8.** Find the probability of an event occurring if there are 5 successful ways in 40 possibilities.

8. _____

**9.** What is the probability of an event that must occur?

9. _____

**10.** *Committee Choice*    You and a friend are in a group of 5 people. One is chosen at random to be on a committee. What is the probability that you or your friend is chosen?

10. _____

**Use your calculator as needed.**

1. Solve the proportion $\dfrac{18}{x-2} = \dfrac{4}{3}$.

1. _____

2. Solve the proportion $\dfrac{x+1}{3} = \dfrac{x+5}{x}$.

2. _____

**In 3–5, give answers to one decimal place where needed.**

3. What is 18% of 180 miles?

3. _____

4. 50 people is what percent of 210 people?

4. _____

5. 90 is 36% of what number?

5. _____

6. **Carpentry**   The weight, $W$, of a plank varies *directly* as its length, $l$. A 7.5 foot plank weighs 30 pounds. Write an equation relating $W$ and $l$.

6. _____

7. $x$ and $y$ vary inversely. If $x = \frac{5}{2}$ when $y = 50$, find an equation relating $x$ and $y$.

7. _____

8. Write the probability of an event which is as likely to occur as not to occur.

8. _____

9. *State Lottery*    In the State Lottery, all three-digit numbers from 000     9. _____
   to 999 have equal chances to win. If your first digit is correct, what
   is the probability your number will be correct on the last two digits
   also?

10. *Marbles in a Jar*    A jar contains 17 blue balls and 51 red balls. If a     10. _____
    ball is removed at random, what is the probability its color is red?

11. Find the *domain* of the rational expression.     11. _____

    $$\frac{2x - 1}{x^2 - 6x}$$

12. Simplify the expression $\frac{x^2 - 9}{x^2 + 3x}$.     12. _____

13. Simplify the expression $\frac{13x^5}{12x^3} \cdot \frac{6x^2}{4x^6}$.     13. _____

14. Simplify the expression $\frac{2(A - 4)}{3} \cdot \frac{3}{8A - 32}$.     14. _____

**15.** Divide $48x^5(x^2 - 1)$ by $44x^3(x - 1)$.

15. _____

**16.** Divide $(18N^3 + 15N^2 - 3N) \div 3N$.

16. _____

**17.** If $\dfrac{x^3 - 18}{x - 2} = x^2 + 2x + 4 - \dfrac{10}{x - 2}$, determine the *quotient* and *remainder*.

17. _____

**18.** Divide $(3x^2 - 2x + 7) \div (x - 2)$.

18. _____

**19.** Solve the equation $x - \dfrac{24}{x} = -2$.

19. _____

**20.** *Average Cost*    You have invested \$40,000 to start a donut shop. You can produce donuts for \$1.10 a dozen. How many dozen must you produce before your average cost per dozen drops to \$1.90?

20. _____

**Use your calculator as needed.**

1. Solve the proportion $\dfrac{3}{x-4} = \dfrac{5}{x}$.

1. _____

2. Solve the proportion $\dfrac{x-1}{3} = \dfrac{x+5}{x-1}$.

2. _____

**In 3–5, give answers to one decimal place where needed.**

3. What is 38% of 1250 yards?

3. _____

4. 82 automobiles is what percent of 920 automobiles?

4. _____

5. 90 is 3.6% of what number?

5. _____

6. **Carpentry**   The volume, $V$, of a tank varies *directly* as its height, $h$. A tank 12 feet high holds 300 cubic feet. Write an equation relating $V$ and $h$.

6. _____

7. $R$ and $S$ vary inversely. If $R$ is 1800 when $S$ is 0.15, find an equation relating $R$ and $S$.

7. _____

8. A test is successful 9 times for every time it fails. Find the probability of failure.

8. _____

**9. State Lottery**    In the State Lottery, all three-digit numbers from 000    9. _____
to 999 have equal chances to win. If your first two digits are correct,
what is the probability the third digit will be correct also?

**10. Marbles in a Jar**    A jar contains 17 blue balls and 68 red balls. If a    10. _____
ball is removed at random, what is the probability its color is blue?

**11.** Find the *domain* of the rational expression.    11. _____

$$\frac{3x - 1}{x^2 + 3x}$$

**12.** Simplify the expression $\dfrac{x^2 + 4x}{x^2 - 16}$.    12. _____

**13.** Simplify the expression $\dfrac{16x^6}{9x^4} \cdot \dfrac{15x}{8x^2}$.    13. _____

**14.** Simplify the expression $\dfrac{2}{x - 3} \cdot \dfrac{2x - 6}{8(x + 4)}$.    14. _____

**15.** Divide $50y^4(y^2 - 4)$ by $45(y + 2)y^3$.

15. _____

**16.** Divide $(21y^4 - 28y^3 + 35y^2) \div (7y)$.

16. _____

**17.** If $\dfrac{x^2 + 4x - 2}{x - 2} = x + 6 + \dfrac{10}{x - 2}$, determine the *quotient* and *remainder*.

17. _____

**18.** Divide $(4x^2 - 7x + 2) \div (x + 1)$.

18. _____

**19.** Solve the equation $x = \dfrac{12}{x + 2} - \dfrac{2x}{x + 2}$.

19. _____

**20. *Average Cost***    You have invested $20,000 to start a donut shop. You can produce donuts for $1.10 a dozen. How many dozen must you produce before your average cost per dozen drops to $1.60?

20. _____

**Use your calculator as needed.**

1. Solve the proportion $\dfrac{x}{2x-1} = \dfrac{5}{3}$.

   1. _____

2. Solve the proportion $\cdot\dfrac{x-1}{x+2} = \dfrac{3}{x}$.

   2. _____

**In 3–5, give answers to one decimal place where needed.**

3. What is 27% of 190 bushels?

   3. _____

4. $3.1 \times 10^{-3}$ is what percent of $8.75 \times 10^{-2}$?

   4. _____

5. 182 is 2.5% of what number?

   5. _____

6. *Carpentry*   The weight, $W$, of a beam varies *directly* as its length, $l$. A 10 foot beam weighs 530 pounds. Write an equation relating $W$ and $l$.

   6. _____

7. $P$ and $Q$ vary inversely. If $P$ is 16.4 when $Q$ is 123, find an equation relating $P$ and $Q$.

   7. _____

8. An event is twice as likely to occur as not to occur. Write the probability it will occur.

   8. _____

9. **State Lottery**    In the State Lottery, all three-digit numbers from 000 to 999 have equal chances to win. What is the probability that the winning number will be a triple (all digits the same)?

9. _____

10. **Marbles in a Jar**    A jar contains 32 blue balls, 14 red balls, and 4 black balls. If a ball is chosen at random, what is the probability it will not be red?

10. _____

11. Find the *domain* of the rational expression.

$$\frac{2x + 3}{x^2 + 3x - 4}$$

11. _____

12. Simplify the expression $\dfrac{(x + 2)^2}{x^2 - 4}$.

12. _____

13. Simplify the expression $\dfrac{15x^3}{8x^5} \div \dfrac{10x^4}{4x}$.

13. _____

14. Simplify the expression $\dfrac{x^2 + 2x + 1}{4x^2 + 4x} \cdot \dfrac{8x}{x^2 - 1}$.

14. _____

**15.** Divide $44x^7(x+2)^2$ by $33x^9(x^2-4)$.

15. _____

**16.** Divide $(36x^4 + 48x^3 - 12x^2) \div (6x^3)$.

16. _____

**17.** If $\dfrac{x^3}{x-2} = x^2 + 2x + 4 + \dfrac{8}{x-2}$, determine the *quotient* and *remainder*.

17. _____

**18.** Divide $(8x^3 + 6x^2 - 3x + 1) \div (2x - 1)$.

18. _____

**19.** Solve the equation $5 - \dfrac{6}{x+3} = \dfrac{3-x}{x^2-9}$.

19. _____

**20.** *Average Cost*   You have invested $50,000 to start a donut shop. Your cost for raw materials is $0.65 per dozen and your overhead costs are $0.55 per dozen. How many dozen must you produce before your average cost per dozen drops to $2.45?

20. _____

1. Decide whether the information defines a function. If it does, state the domain of the function.

| input | 0 | 1 | 2 | 3 |
|-------|---|---|---|---|
| output | 1 | 1 | 2 | 2 |

1. _____

2. Is a function defined by $\{(0,\ 0),\ (1,\ 1),\ (1,\ 2),\ (2,\ 3)\}$?

2. _____

3. $f(x) = 3x^2 - 7x + 6$. Find $f(2)$.

3. _____

4. Does the graph represent $y$ as a function of $x$?

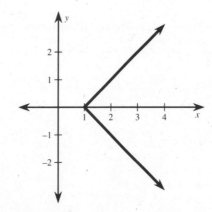

4. _____

5. Find the equation for the linear function with
   $f(-3) = 2$ and $f(1) = 4$.

5. _____

6. Describe the relationship between the graph of $f$ and the graph of $g$. (It is not necessary to sketch the graphs.)
   $f(x) = 7^x$, $g(x) = 1 + 7^x$

6. _____

7. Find the *vertex* of the graph of the function. Is the vertex the highest or lowest point?
   $f(x) = 2(x + 2)^2 - 7$

7. _____

8. Sketch the graph of the function.
   $f(x) = -x^2 + 2x + 2$.
   What is the maximum value of this function?

8. _____
   *Use graph at left.*

© D.C. Heath and Company *Algebra 1*

Name _____

Date _____

1. Decide whether the information defines a function. If it does, state the domain of the function.

| input | a | b | c | d |
|-------|---|---|---|---|
| output | 2 | 4 | 2 | 6 |

1. _____

2. Is a function defined by $\{(1, 4), (1, 3), (2, 2), (3, 1)\}$?

2. _____

3. $f(x) = -4x^2 + 8x + 5$. Find $f(2)$.

3. _____

4. Does the graph represent $y$ as a function of $x$?

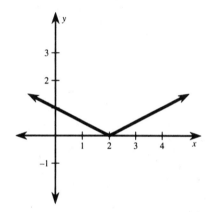

4. _____

5. Find the equation for the linear function with $f(-2) = 5$ *and* $f(3) = 3$.

5. _____

6. Describe the relationship between the graph of $f$ and the graph of $g$. (It is not necessary to sketch the graphs.)
$f(x) = 7^x$, $g(x) = -7^x$

6. _____

7. Find the *vertex* of the graph of the function. Is the vertex the highest or lowest point?
$f(x) = -2(x - 3)^2 + 4$.

7. _____

8. Sketch the graph of the function.
$f(x) = x^2 - 4x + 2$

What is the minimum value of this function?

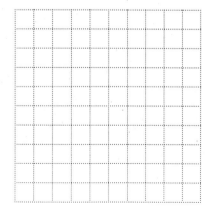

8. _____
*Use graph at left.*

1. Decide whether the graph represents $y$ as a function of $x$.

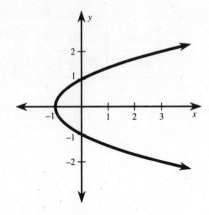

1. _____

2. Decide whether the information defines a function. If it does, state the domain of the function.

| input | 0 | 1 | 2 | 3 | 4 |
|-------|---|---|---|---|---|
| output | 1 | 2 | 3 | 2 | 1 |

2. _____

3. Evaluate $f(-3)$.

$$f(x) = 2x^2 + 4x - 7$$

3. _____

4. Find the slope of the graph of the linear function.

$$f(-2) = 7, \ f(3) = -1$$

4. _____

5. Find an equation for the linear function.

$$f(1) = -4, \ f(2) = 6$$

5. _____

6. Sketch the graph of the linear function.

$$f(x) = -\tfrac{2}{3}x + 3$$

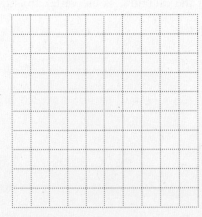

6. *Use graph at left.*

In 7–9, describe the relationship between the graph of $f$ and the graph of $g$. **(It is not necessary to sketch the graphs.)**

**7.** $f(x) = 2^x$, $g(x) = -2^x$

7. _____

**8.** $f(x) = 2^x$, $g(x) = 2^{x-1}$

8. _____

**9.** $f(x) = 2^x$, $g(x) = 5 + 2^x$

9. _____

**In 10 and 11, sketch the graph of the function.**

**10.** $f(x) = 2^x$

10. *Use graph at left.*

**11.** $g(x) = -2^x$

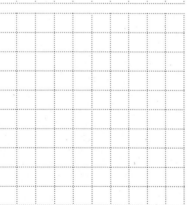

11. *Use graph at left.*

**12.** Find the *vertex* of the graph of the function. Is the vertex the highest or lowest point?

$$f(x) = -2(x + 3)^2 + 7$$

12. _____

**13.** Write the function

$$f(x) = x^2 + 4x$$

in completed square form.
Then sketch its graph.

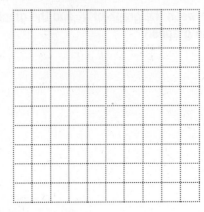

**13.** _____
*Use graph at left.*

**14.** Find the center and asymptotes of the hyperbola.

$$f(x) = \frac{1}{x - 4} + 5$$

**14.** _____

**15.** *Florist Shops*   Gary's Florist
Shop has 5 employees and is
hiring new employees at the
rate of 1 per year. Ray's Florist
Shop has 2 employees and is
hiring new employees at the
rate of 2 per year. Write a
model that gives the ratio of the
number of Gary's employees
to Ray's. Sketch the graph of
this model over the interval
$0 \le x \le 4$, where $x$ represents
the number of years.

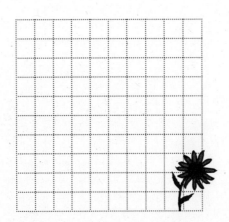

**15.** _____
*Use graph at left.*

**16.** Use polynomial division to
help sketch the graph of the
function.

$$f(x) = \frac{4x + 3}{x + 1}.$$

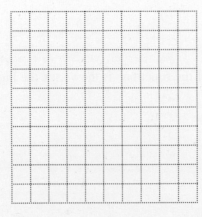

**16.** *Use graph at left.*

**17.** Find the median of the collection of numbers.

17, 24, 18, 36, 4, 52, 19, 29, 18

17. _____

**18.** Construct a stem-and-leaf plot for the data. Use the result to list the data in *decreasing* order.

75, 24, 38, 19, 75, 27, 13, 82, 97, 14, 98, 71, 65, 63,
51, 44, 59, 29, 72, 37, 14, 88, 67, 54, 49, 34, 71, 65

18. _____

***Days of Rain*** **For 19 and 20, use the data as described. An observer noted the number of rain days for each month of a year as follows:**

**January–5, February–8, March–12,
April–12, May–8, June–7,
July–8, August–3, September–12,
October–10, November–7,
December–8.**

**19.** Find the *mean* monthly rain days for the year.

19. _____

**20.** Find the *median* and the *mode* for the monthly number of rain days for the year.

20. _____

Name _____

Date _____

1. Decide whether the graph represents $y$ as a function of $x$.

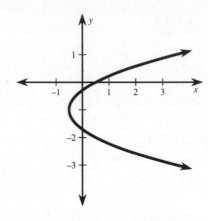

1. _____

2. Decide whether the information defines a function. If it does, state the domain of the function.

| *input* | a | b | c | d |
|---------|---|---|---|---|
| *output* | 0 | 1 | 0 | 1 |

2. _____

3. Evaluate $f(3)$.

$$f(x) = -3x^2 + 10x - 2$$

3. _____

4. Find the slope of the graph of the linear function.

$$f(-3) = -2, \quad f(3) = 2$$

4. _____

5. Find an equation for the linear function.

$$f(-3) = -9, \quad f(3) = 1$$

5. _____

6. Sketch the graph of the linear function.

$$f(x) = -\tfrac{1}{3}x + 1$$

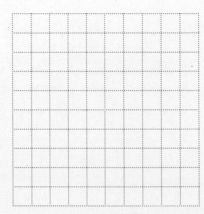

6. *Use graph at left.*

In 7–9, describe the relationship between the graph of $f$ and the graph of $g$. (It is not necessary to sketch the graphs.)

**7.** $f(x) = 3^x$, $g(x) = 3^{x-2}$                    7. _____

**8.** $f(x) = 3^x$, $g(x) = 3^x - 4$                    8. _____

**9.** $f(x) = 3^x$, $g(x) = -3^x$                    9. _____

In 10 and 11, sketch the graph of the function.

**10.** $f(x) = -3^x$

10.  *Use graph at left.*

**11.** $g(x) = 3^x + 1$

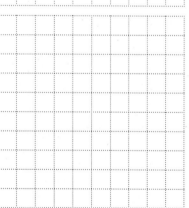

11.  *Use graph at left.*

**12.** Find the *vertex* of the graph of the function. Is the vertex the highest or lowest point?

$$f(x) = 4(x-2)^2 - 7$$

12. _____

**13.** Write the function

$$f(x) = x^2 - 6x + 13$$

in completed square form. Then sketch its graph.

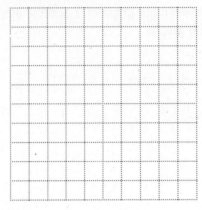

**13.** _____
*Use graph at left.*

**14.** Find the center and asymptotes of the hyperbola.

$$f(x) = \frac{1}{x+3} - 4$$

**14.** _____

**15.** *Florist Shops*    Mary's Florist Shop has 6 employees and is hiring new employees at the rate of 1 per year. Joy's Florist Shop has 3 employees and is hiring new employees at the rate of 2 per year. Write a model that gives the ratio of the number of Mary's employees to Joy's. Sketch the graph of this model over the interval $0 \le x \le 4$, where $x$ represents the number of years.

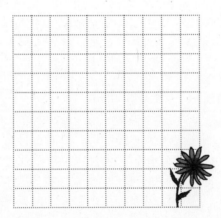

**15.** _____
*Use graph at left.*

**16.** Use polynomial division to help sketch the graph of the function.

$$f(x) = \frac{x}{x-1}$$

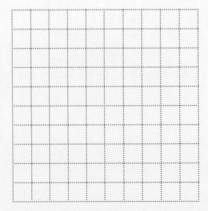

**16.** *Use graph at left.*

**17.** Find the median of the collection of numbers.                    17. _____
   33, 42, 18, 75, 16, 92, 78, 33, 64

**18.** Construct a stem-and-leaf plot for the data. Use the result to list the       18. _____
   data in *decreasing* order.
      49, 64, 33, 27, 81, 97, 24, 25, 33, 78, 65, 55, 59, 41,
      65, 28, 44, 87, 51, 47, 60, 77, 21, 43, 67, 56, 94, 40

***Days of Rain***   For 19 and 20, use the data as described. An observer
noted the number of rain days for each month of a year as follows:

January–5, February–7, March–8,
April–11, May–8, June–5,
July–7, August–4, September–5,
October–8, November–6,
December–6.

**19.** Find the *mean* monthly rain days for the year.                    19. _____

**20.** Find the *median* and the *mode* for the monthly number of rain days       20. _____
   for the year.

1. Decide whether the graph represents $y$ as a function of $x$.

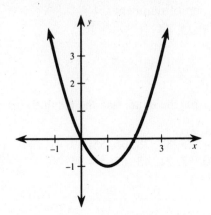

1. _____

2. Decide whether the information defines a function. If it does, state the domain of the function.

| input | a | b | a | c |
|-------|---|---|---|---|
| output | 0 | 1 | 2 | 1 |

2. _____

3. Evaluate $f(-4)$.

$$f = -2x^2 - 5x + 12$$

3. _____

4. Find the slope of the graph of the linear function.

$$f(-3) = 2, \ f(5) = -2$$

4. _____

5. Find an equation for the linear function.

$$f(5) = -1, \ f(-1) = -3$$

5. _____

6. Sketch the graph of the linear function.

$$f(x) = \tfrac{1}{4}x - 1$$

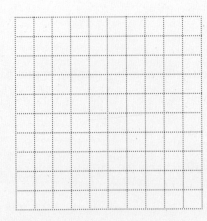

6. *Use graph at left.*

© D.C. Heath and Company *Algebra 1*

**In 7–9, describe the relationship between the graph of $f$ and the graph of $g$. (It is not necessary to sketch the graphs.)**

**7.** $f(x) = \left(\frac{1}{2}\right)^x$, $g(x) = \frac{1}{2} + \left(\frac{1}{2}\right)^x$

7. _____

**8.** $f(x) = \left(\frac{1}{2}\right)^x$, $g(x) = -\left(\frac{1}{2}\right)^x$

8. _____

**9.** $f(x) = \left(\frac{1}{2}\right)^x$, $g(x) = \left(\frac{1}{2}\right)^{x+3}$

9. _____

**In 10 and 11, sketch the graph of the function.**

**10.** $f(x) = 1 + \left(\frac{1}{2}\right)^x$

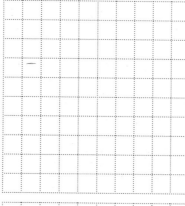

10. _*Use graph at left.*_

**11.** $g(x) = 2^{x-2}$

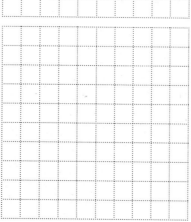

11. _*Use graph at left.*_

**12.** Find the *vertex* of the graph of the function.  Is the vertex the highest or lowest point?

$$f(x) = -\frac{1}{4}\left(x - \frac{1}{2}\right)^2 + \frac{7}{4}$$

12. _____

**13.** Write the function

$$f(x) = -x^2 + 2x + 2$$

in completed square form.
Then sketch its graph.

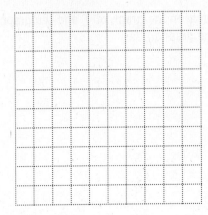

**13.** _____
*Use graph at left.*

**14.** Find the center and asymptotes of the hyperbola.

$$f(x) = \frac{2}{x-3} - 6$$

**14.** _____

**15.** *Florist Shops*    Tom's Florist
Shop has 4 employees and is
hiring new employees at the
rate of 1 per year. Ron's Florist
Shop has 3 employees and is
hiring new employees at the
rate of 2 per year. Write a
model that gives the ratio of
the number of Tom's employees
to Ron's.  Sketch the graph of
this model over the interval
$0 \le x \le 6$, where $x$ represents
the number of years.

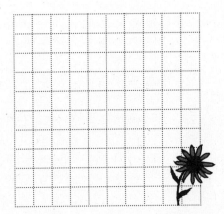

**15.** _____
*Use graph at left.*

**16.** Use polynomial division to
help sketch the graph of the
function.

$$f(x) = \frac{3-x}{x-2}$$

**16.** _____*Use graph at left.*_____

**17.** Find the median of the collection of numbers.

    40, 54, 9, 48, 37, 81, 16, 38, 29, 30

17. _____

**18.** Construct a stem-and-leaf plot for the data. Use the result to list the data in *increasing* order.

    37, 28, 76, 80, 52, 67, 44, 71, 64, 52, 29, 33, 59, 47, 35,
    25, 69, 75, 41, 63, 59, 63, 44, 71, 22, 20, 32, 70

18. _____

***Days of Rain***    For 19 and 20, use the data as described. An observer noted the number of rain days for each month of a year as follows:

January–4, February–5, March–7,
April–12, May–9, June–8,
July–4, August–4, September–4,
October–10, November–9,
December–6.

**19.** Find the *mean* monthly rain days for the year.

19. _____

**20.** Find the *median* and the *mode* for the monthly number of rain days for the year.

20. _____

1. State whether the system represents parallel lines, intersecting lines, or a single line. Also state whether there is one, none, or many solutions.

    $$\begin{cases} 3x + 4y = 5 \\ 6x + 8y = 5 \end{cases}$$

    1. _____

2. Solve the linear system.

    $$\begin{cases} 3x - 5y = 14 \\ 2x + 3y = 3 \end{cases}$$

    2. _____

3. Solve the linear system.

    $$\begin{cases} 2x - 5y = 6 \\ -6x + 15y = -18 \end{cases}$$

    3. _____

4. **Amount Invested** A total of $20,000 is invested in two funds paying 6% and 7% annual interest. The combined interest is $1325. How much of the $20,000 is invested in each fund?

    4. _____

5. Sketch the graph of the constraints. Label the vertices of the graph.

    $$\begin{cases} y \le \frac{1}{5}x + \frac{12}{5} \\ y \ge -x \\ y \ge 2x - 3 \end{cases}$$

    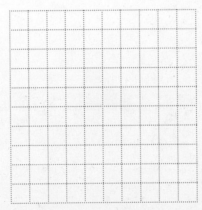

    5. _Use graph at left._

ⓒ D.C. Heath and Company *Algebra 1*

**6.** Find the maximum value of the objective quantity $C$.

$C = -2x + 4y$
  Constraints
$$\begin{cases} x \geq -1 \\ x \leq \phantom{-}3 \\ y \geq \phantom{-}0 \\ y \leq \phantom{-}x + 2 \end{cases}$$

**6.** _____
  *Use graph at left.*

**7.** Simplify $(3x^2)^4 \left( \dfrac{1}{27x^3} \right)^2$.

**7.** _____

**8.** Rewrite $\dfrac{4^0(y^{-2})^4}{x^{-5}}$ using positive exponents.

**8.** _____

**9.** Solve for $x$.

$5^3 \cdot 5^x \cdot (5^3)^2 = (25)^6$

**9.** _____

**10.** Simplify the expression.

$\dfrac{8a^3b^2}{-2^2b^4} \cdot \dfrac{-8a^4b^3}{32a^5b^2}$

**10.** _____

11. Rewrite 794,000,000,000,000 in scientific notation.

11. _____

12. Evaluate $(7 \times 10^{-5})(9 \times 10^7)$. Write the result in decimal form.

12. _____

13. Evaluate $(7.32 \times 10^6)^3$. Write the result in scientific notation.

13. _____

14. **Pioneer 10**    On March 1, 1992, the Pioneer 10 spacecraft was still sending signals back to Earth on the 20th anniversary of its launch. The signals took about $7\frac{1}{2}$ hours to reach Earth. If radio waves travel at $1.87 \times 10^5$ miles per second, find the approximate distance the spacecraft had traveled. (1 hr $= 3.6 \times 10^3$ seconds.)

14. _____

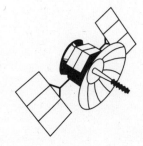

15. **Balance in Account**    A principal of $800 is deposited in an account that pays 5.4% annual interest compounded yearly. Find the balance after 6 years.

15. _____

16. **Deposit in Account**    How much must you deposit in an account that pays 6% annual interest compounded yearly to have a balance of $1000 after 10 years?

16. _____

**17.** Choose the equation that represents *exponential decay*.

    **a.** $y = (1.67)^t$   **b.** $y = (0.67)^t$

17. _____

**18.** Find all of the square roots of the number 0.81.

18. _____

**19.** Evaluate the expression to two decimal places.

$$\frac{21 - 5\sqrt{3}}{4}$$

19. _____

**20.** Solve the equation. Round your answer to two decimal places.

    $8x^2 = 113$

20. _____

**21.** Sketch the graph of the equation. Label the vertex.

    $y = x^2 + 2x - 2$

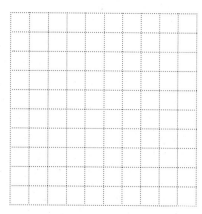

21.   *Use graph at left.*

**22.** Use the quadratic formula to solve the equation. Round your answer to two decimal places.

    $x^2 + 2x - 5 = 0$

22. _____

**23.** Sketch the graph of the inequality.

$$y \geq \tfrac{1}{4}(x+1)(x-4)$$

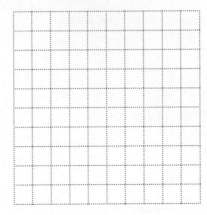

**23.** _Use graph at left._

**24.** Perform the indicated operations.

$$5(2x-3) - 2(x+4) + 3(1-3x)$$

**24.** _____

**25.** Multiply $(3x-5)(2x+3)$.

**25.** _____

**26.** Multiply $-x^2(-2x^2 + x - 3)$.

**26.** _____

**27.** Find the greatest common factor of the three terms.

$$30A^5B^3, \; 75A^3B^6, \; 45A^4B^2$$

**27.** _____

**28.** Factor the expression $4y^2 - 49$.

**28.** _____

**29.** Factor the expression $2x^2 - 16xy + 32y^2$.

**29.** _____

**30.** Solve the equation $4x^2 + 4x - 3 = 0$.

30. _____

**31.** Solve the equation $7x^2 - 2x = 0$.

31. _____

**32.** *Garden Dimensions*   The length of a rectangular garden is 25 feet longer than the width. If it covers an area of 2600 square feet, find the length and width.

32. _____

**33.** Solve the proportion $\dfrac{7}{x-3} = \dfrac{4}{x}$.

33. _____

**34.** 60 is what percent of 250?

34. _____

**35.** 48 is 30% of what number?

35. _____

**36.** $x$ and $y$ vary *inversely*. If $x = 2.4$ when $y = 130$, find an equation relating $x$ and $y$.

36. _____

**37.** An event is twice as likely to occur as not to occur. Find the probability that the event does not occur.

37. _____

**38.** *Marbles in a Jar*   A jar contains 9 marbles numbered 1 through 9. If one marble is removed at random, what is the probability it will carry an odd number?

38. _____

**39.** Find the domain of the rational expression.

$$\frac{x^2 + 4}{x^2 + 4x}$$

39. _____

**40.** Simplify $\dfrac{3x^3(y - 3)}{5y^2x^2} \cdot \dfrac{15y^3}{(4y - 12)}$.

40. _____

**41.** Divide $(15A^3 - 12A^2 - 9A) \div 3A^2$.

41. _____

**42.** Is a function defined by $\{(-2,\ 3),\ (0,\ 1),\ (2,\ -2),\ (4,\ 2)\}$? If so, state its domain.

42. _____

**43.** $f(x) = -2x^2 + 7x + 5$. Find $f\left(\frac{3}{2}\right)$.

43. _____

**44.** Find the equation for the linear function.
$$f(4) = -1, \ f(-2) = -4$$

44. _____

**45.** Sketch the graph of
$$f(x) = 1 - 2^x.$$

45. *Use graph at left.*

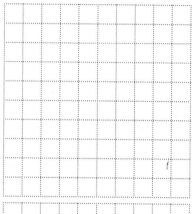

**46.** Sketch the graph of
$$f(x) = \frac{3}{x-1} + 2.$$
List the asymptotes.

46. _____
*Use graph at left.*

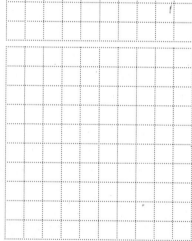

**47.** For the collection of weights of dogs, find the *mean, median,* and the *mode.*

| 27 | 32 | 14 | 28 | 35 |
| 28 | 15 | 21 | 41 | 32 |
| 20 | 10 | 30 | 32 | 40 |

47. _____

Name _____

Date _____

1. Find the distance between the two points.

    $(-4, 7)$, $(2, 4)$

1. _____

2. Decide whether the three points are vertices of a right triangle.

    $(1, -5)$, $(-2, 1)$, $(-4, 0)$

2. _____

3. Find the midpoint between the two points.

    $(3, -6)$, $(4, 2)$

3. _____

4. Simplify the radical expression.

    $\sqrt{\dfrac{13}{32}}$

4. _____

5. Perform the indicated operations. Simplify your result.

    $\sqrt{3} \cdot \sqrt{5} \cdot \sqrt{30}$

5. _____

6. Simplify the expression.

    $2\sqrt{48} - \sqrt{12} + \sqrt{75}$

6. _____

7. Solve the equation.

    $x - 1 = \sqrt{4x + 1}$

7. _____

8. **Geometry**   A box is made so that its length is the geometric mean of its height and width. If the height is 8 and the width is 5, find the length.

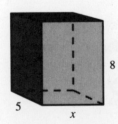

8. _____

Name _____

Date _____

**1.** Find the distance between the two points.

$(-5, \ 3), \ (-1, \ 5)$

1. _____

**2.** Decide whether the three points are vertices of a right triangle.

$(1, \ 0), \ (3, \ 1), \ (2, \ 3)$

2. _____

**3.** Find the midpoint between the two points.

$(5, \ -3), \ (7, \ 4)$

3. _____

**4.** Simplify the radical expression.

$\sqrt{\dfrac{3}{72}}$

4. _____

**5.** Perform the indicated operations. Simplify your result.

$\sqrt{7} \cdot \sqrt{2} \cdot \sqrt{42}$

5. _____

**6.** Simplify the expression.

$\sqrt{32} + 3\sqrt{18} - 2\sqrt{50}$

6. _____

**7.** Solve the equation.

$x - 2 = \sqrt{3x + 4}$

7. _____

**8.** *Geometry*    A box is made so that its length is the geometric mean of its height and width. If the height is 10 and the width is 6, find the length.

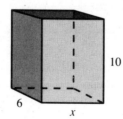

8. _____

1. Find the distance between the two points.

   $(-4, -2)$, $(2, 3)$

   1. _____

2. Decide whether the three points are the vertices of a right triangle.

   $(2, 0)$, $(-1, -1)$, $(1, 3)$

   2. _____

3. Find the midpoint between the two points.

   $(-2, 5)$, $(3, -4)$

   3. _____

4. Simplify the radical expression.

   $\sqrt{\frac{20}{27}}$

   4. _____

5. Perform the indicated operations and simplify the result.

   $\left(\sqrt{2} + \sqrt{3}\right)\sqrt{6}$

   5. _____

6. Simplify.

   $\dfrac{3\sqrt{20}}{\sqrt{36}}$

   6. _____

7. **Geometry**  Find the area of the rectangle.

   $\sqrt{8} + \sqrt{12}$

   $\sqrt{6}$

   7. _____

**8.** Evaluate $f(x) = x^2 + x - 2$, when $x = 1 + \sqrt{3}$.

8. _____

**9.** Solve the equation, if possible.

$$\sqrt{2x + 7} = 5$$

9. _____

**10.** Solve the equation, if possible.

$$\sqrt{1 - 2x} = -4$$

10. _____

**11.** *Geometry*   One side of a triangle is the geometric mean of the other two sides, as shown. Find the length of side $x$ (the mean).

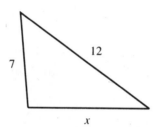

11. _____

**12.** Find $\tan A$ and $\tan B$.

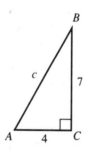

12. _____

**13.** Find $\tan 38.8°$ to three decimal places.

13. _____

**14. _Geometry_**   Find side *c* to two decimal places in the triangle shown.

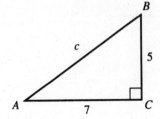

14. _____

**15. _Geometry_**   In the triangle shown, $\tan A = \frac{4}{9}$. Find side *b*.

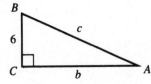

15. _____

**16.** At a distance of 10.8 meters from a tree, the angle of elevation to the top of the tree is 26°. How tall is the tree?

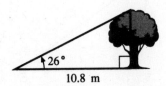

16. _____

**17.** If *a* and *b* are real numbers, what axiom justifies the statement?

$$a + b = b + a$$

17. _____

**18.** Give a counterexample to show the statement is not always true for real numbers *a* and *b*.

$$(a + b)^2 = a^2 + b^2$$

18. _____

**Name** _____

**Date** _____

1. Find the distance between the two points.

   $(-5,\ 3),\ (4,\ -1)$

   1. _____

2. Decide whether the three points are the vertices of a right triangle.

   $(-4,\ 4),\ (3,\ 1),\ (-2,\ -1)$

   2. _____

3. Find the midpoint between the two points.

   $(7,\ -3),\ (5,\ 4)$

   3. _____

4. Simplify the radical expression.

   $\sqrt{\frac{27}{8}}$

   4. _____

5. Perform the indicated operations and simplify the result.

   $\sqrt{8}\left(\sqrt{2}+\sqrt{3}\right)$

   5. _____

6. Simplify.

   $\dfrac{\sqrt{24}}{3\sqrt{12}}$

   6. _____

7. Find the area of the rectangle.

   _____

**8.** Evaluate $f(x) = x^2 + x - 2$, when $x = 1 - \sqrt{3}$.

8. _____

**9.** Solve the equation, if possible.

$$\sqrt{3x - 5} = 5$$

9. _____

**10.** Solve the equation, if possible.

$$\sqrt{2 - 3x} = -4$$

10. _____

**11. Geometry**    One side of a triangle is the geometric mean of the other two sides, as shown. Find the length of side $x$ (the mean).

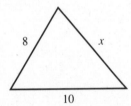

11. _____

**12.** Find tan $A$ and tan $B$.

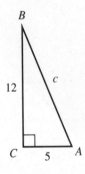

12. _____

**13.** Find tan 16.4° to two decimal places.

13. _____

**14. *Geometry***    Find side $c$ to two decimal places in the triangle shown.

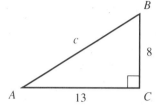

14. _____

**15.** At a distance of 27.4 feet from a tree, the angle of elevation to the top of the tree is 40°. How tall is the tree?

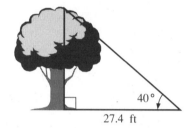

15. _____

**16.** In the triangle shown, $\tan A = \frac{5}{11}$. Find side $b$.

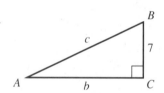

16. _____

**17.** If $a$ and $b$ are real numbers, what axiom justifies the statement?

$a \cdot b = b \cdot a$

17. _____

**18.** Give a counterexample to show the statement is not always true for real numbers $a$ and $b$.

$(a - b)^2 = a^2 - b^2$

18. _____

1. Find the distance between the two points.

   $\left(\frac{3}{2},\ -\frac{1}{4}\right),\ (2,\ 1)$

   1. _____

2. Decide whether the three points are the vertices of a right triangle.

   $(-1,\ 4),\ (2,\ -3),\ (3,\ 0)$

   2. _____

3. Find the midpoint between the two points.

   $\left(\frac{2}{3},\ 4\right),\ \left(-\frac{5}{3},\ -3\right)$

   3. _____

4. Simplify the radical expression.

   $\sqrt{\frac{98}{27}}$

   4. _____

5. Perform the indicated operations and simplify the result.

   $\left(\sqrt{5} - \sqrt{3}\right)\sqrt{15}$

   5. _____

6. Simplify.

   $\dfrac{2\sqrt{18}}{\sqrt{32}}$

   6. _____

7. **Geometry**   Find the area of the rectangle.

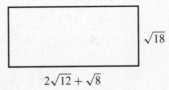

$2\sqrt{12} + \sqrt{8}$

$\sqrt{18}$

   7. _____

**8.** Evaluate $f(x) = x^2 - 2x - 3$, when $x = -1 + \sqrt{2}$.

8. _____

**9.** Solve the equation, if possible.

$\sqrt{9 - 2x} = -2$

9. _____

**10.** Solve the equation, if possible.

$\sqrt{2 - x} = 2 - x$

10. _____

**11. *Geometry*** One side of a triangle is the geometric mean of the other two sides, as shown. Find the length of side $x$ (the mean).

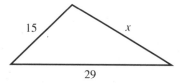

11. _____

**12.** Find $\tan A$ and $\tan B$.

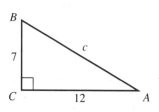

12. _____

**13.** Find $\tan 62.3°$ to three decimal places.

13. _____

**14.** *Geometry*   Find side $c$ to two decimal places and find angle $A$. Use your calculator.

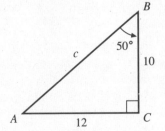

14. _____

**15.** *Geometry*   In the triangle shown, find angle $B$ and side $b$ to one decimal place.

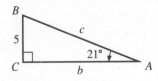

15. _____

**16.** *Geometry*   In the triangle shown, $\tan B = \frac{5}{2}$. Find the lengths of sides $b$ and $c$ to one decimal place.

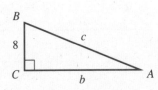

16. _____

**17.** If $a$, $b$, and $c$ are real numbers, what axiom justifies the statement?

$$(a + b) + c = a + (b + c)$$

17. _____

**18.** Give a counterexample to show the statement is not always true for real numbers $a$, $b$, and $c$.

If $a < b$, then $ac < bc$.

18. _____

# Strategies for Taking College Entrance Tests

**Do your schoolwork.**

College entrance mathematics tests are based on the concepts and skills taught in high school mathematics courses. The best way to prepare for a college entrance test is to keep up with your regular studies.

**Learn about the exam.**

You will be more prepared for taking the test if you are familiar with the directions and the format of the questions. This will reduce your anxiety and allow you to concentrate on the test questions and improve your chances of getting a good score.

While taking this algebra course, use the *Practice for College Entrance Tests* that are correlated with each chapter. These sample questions cover the topics you are currently learning.

Read the free booklets provided with the registration packets for the Scholastic Aptitude Test (SAT) or the American College Testing Assessment (ACT). These booklets are called *Taking the SAT* and *Preparing for the ACT Assessment*. They contain current information about the test you will take and a sample test. Many test preparation books, materials, and programs are also available that provide practice in taking college entrance tests. If you want additional practice, you can obtain materials from your school or public library. Your teacher and the guidance department at your school will also be able to provide information about test preparation programs and materials.

Study the directions in each section of the sample exam. This will save you time during the test since the directions printed in the registration booklets are the same as the directions that will appear on the test that you take.

**Pace yourself.**

Don't get bogged down in one question. If the question seems too difficult, skip it and go back after you have answered the other questions. When you go back to tackle a more difficult question, you may get an insight that you didn't have when you first read the question.

Don't rush through the test. Be sure you read each question and the possible answers. Decide how you want to check your pace. Don't, however, check the clock after answering each question. This tends to use time and increase anxiety. You might consider checking the time after every ten questions. Because the easier questions tend to be at the beginning of the test, you should try to allow more time for the later questions. Not all test taking sites have clocks on the wall, so you may want to bring a watch. Don't panic if you do not have time to answer all the questions. It is possible to receive a high score on a test without answering every question.

**Make notes in the booklet.**

When working on a question, make notes in the test booklet of what you do know. Label graphs and geometric figures with known and deduced information. If you decide to skip the question, this information will help refresh your memory when you return to it. To help avoid marking responses incorrectly, you should also circle the answer to each question in the test booklet.

**Don't make wild guesses.**

On some college entrance tests a fraction of a point is deducted for each wrong answer. If you don't know the answer to a question, try to eliminate one or two of the answer choices to increase the probability of choosing the correct answer. Then use your best judgement to choose the answer to the question from the remaining choices.

**Check your work.**

Once you have answered all the questions to a section in the test, use the remaining time to check the work you have done. This is the only time you will be allowed to review your notes and make changes. You are not permitted to return to a section of the test after the time has expired.

To check your work, first make sure that you have answered all the questions in the section and have indicated only one answer for each question. Look for and remove any stray pencil marks that could affect the scoring of the test.

Next, review each problem and check any calculations you have made. This checking will be easier if you made clear notes in the test booklet when you originally worked the problem.

**Know your calculator.**

Some college entrance tests allow the optional use of calculators. Remember that a calculator is only a tool—it cannot answer the questions for you. The calculator that you bring to the test should be one that you have used. Be sure that it uses the order of operations that you expect. For instance, if you enter $4 + 6/2 - 1 =$, does your calculator display 6 or 4? If it displays 6, then it is using the correct order of operations, $4 + (6/2) - 1 = 6$. If it displays 4, then it is using the following order of operations: $[(4+6)/2] - 1 = 4$. The important thing is that you must know how the calculator you are using works. When you use a calculator, be careful to press the correct keys.

**Relax the night before.**

On the night before the exam, gather together any items you will need for the test: pencils with erasers, your admission ticket, identification, directions to the test center, glasses for reading, a watch to pace yourself, and (if allowed) a calculator with *fresh batteries*.

Don't try to cram the night before the test. Do something that you find relaxing. Get a good night's sleep and eat breakfast in the morning.

# Instructions for Recording
# Student-Generated Responses

**1994 SAT Test**    Starting in the spring of 1994, the Scholastic Aptitude Test will include 10 student-produced response questions. The student will solve the problem and then write the answer in a grid. Below are some sample questions and answers to demonstrate how to use the grid. In each case, notice that you write your answer at the top of the grid. Next, fill in completely the corresponding ellipses in the column. The answer may be an integer, a decimal, or a fraction.

**1.**

If the eighth number in the list is 47, and if each number after the first number in the list is 3 less than the number preceding it, what is the fourth number in the list?

Answer: 59

**2.**

Apples are sold 8 for $1. At this rate if 2 apples are bought and paid for with a $10.00 bill, what is the correct change, in dollars? (Assume no tax.)

Answer: 9.75

**3.**

An oatmeal cookie recipe calls for 1 cup of raisins for every 3 cups of flour. If a small batch of cookies is desired using only 1 cup of flour, how many cups of raisins should be used?

Answer: $\frac{1}{3}$

1.

2.

3.

4.

5.

6.

7.

8.

9.

10.

11.

12.

**Fill in the circle of the letter that corresponds to the correct answer.**

1. Which fraction is less than $\frac{3}{8}$?

   **A.** $\frac{11}{24}$    **B.** $\frac{1}{3}$    **C.** $\frac{5}{12}$    **D.** $\frac{5}{6}$    **E.** $\frac{21}{56}$

   1. Ⓐ Ⓑ Ⓒ Ⓓ Ⓔ

2. Which integer is between $\frac{25}{3}$ and $\frac{19}{2}$?

   **A.** 5    **B.** 6    **C.** 7    **D.** 8    **E.** 9

   2. Ⓐ Ⓑ Ⓒ Ⓓ Ⓔ

3. Arrange in increasing order:

   I. $\frac{5}{11}$    II. 25%    III. $\frac{1}{0.25}$    IV. $\frac{11}{5}$

   **A.** I, IV, III, II    **B.** III, I, IV, II    **C.** III, II, I, IV
   **D.** III, I, II, IV    **E.** II, I, IV, III

   3. Ⓐ Ⓑ Ⓒ Ⓓ Ⓔ

4. Sally's grades for the first five math tests this quarter were 92, 96, 85, 89, and 93. What was her average test grade for the quarter?

   **A.** 88    **B.** 89    **C.** 90    **D.** 91    **E.** 92

   4. Ⓐ Ⓑ Ⓒ Ⓓ Ⓔ

5. Which of the following expresses 90 as the product of prime numbers?

   **A.** $1 \times 3 \times 5 \times 6$    **B.** $2 \times 3 \times 3 \times 5$    **C.** $2 \times 5 \times 9$
   **D.** $2 \times 2 \times 3 \times 5$    **E.** $2 \times 3 \times 15$

   5. Ⓐ Ⓑ Ⓒ Ⓓ Ⓔ

6. The average of 5 numbers is 7. The average of 7 numbers is 5. What is the average of all twelve numbers?

   **A.** $5\frac{5}{6}$    **B.** 6    **C.** $6\frac{5}{6}$    **D.** 7    **E.** $7\frac{1}{6}$

   6. Ⓐ Ⓑ Ⓒ Ⓓ Ⓔ

7. 144 is 40% of what?

   **A.** 720    **B.** 360    **C.** 288    **D.** 240    **E.** 57.6

   7. Ⓐ Ⓑ Ⓒ Ⓓ Ⓔ

8. Yvonne bought 5 pencils at $b$ cents each and 2 erasers at $c$ cents each. Which expression represents the amount of money Yvonne spent?

   **A.** $5b$    **B.** $2c$    **C.** $5c + 2b$    **D.** $7b$    **E.** $5b + 2c$

   8. Ⓐ Ⓑ Ⓒ Ⓓ Ⓔ

9. If $x = 6$, then $4x + 5 = $ ⬚ ?

   **A.** 29    **B.** 27    **C.** 25    **D.** 23    **E.** 17

   9. Ⓐ Ⓑ Ⓒ Ⓓ Ⓔ

10. Which set only contains divisors of 54?

    **A.** {2, 3, 6, 7}    **B.** {2, 6, 8, 9}    **C.** {2, 3, 6, 9}
    **D.** {1, 2, 3, 7}    **E.** {2, 3, 5, 6}

    10. Ⓐ Ⓑ Ⓒ Ⓓ Ⓔ

If Column A is greater than Column B, fill in the circle for A.
If Column B is greater than Column A, fill in the circle for B.
If Column A is equal to Column B, fill in the circle for C.
If there is not enough information, fill in the circle for D.
Information centered between the columns concerns the quantities in both columns.

| | Column A | Column B | | | | | |
|---|---|---|---|---|---|---|---|
| 1. | The product of 4 and 2 | The sum of 3 and 3 | 1. | Ⓐ | Ⓑ | Ⓒ | Ⓓ |
| 2. | $4 + 3 \cdot 6 - 10$ | $(4 + 3) \cdot 6 - 10$ | 2. | Ⓐ | Ⓑ | Ⓒ | Ⓓ |

3.

$$x = 3, \; y = 2$$

| | Column A | Column B | | | | | |
|---|---|---|---|---|---|---|---|
| | $2x + 3y$ | $y(x + 3)$ | 3. | Ⓐ | Ⓑ | Ⓒ | Ⓓ |
| 4. | $\frac{2}{3}$ | $0.66$ | 4. | Ⓐ | Ⓑ | Ⓒ | Ⓓ |
| 5. | The quotient of 15 and 3 | 5 | 5. | Ⓐ | Ⓑ | Ⓒ | Ⓓ |
| 6. | Area of a square with side $x$ | Area of a circle with radius $y$ | 6. | Ⓐ | Ⓑ | Ⓒ | Ⓓ |

7.

$$a < 20, \; b > 17$$

| | Column A | Column B | | | | | |
|---|---|---|---|---|---|---|---|
| | $a$ | $b$ | 7. | Ⓐ | Ⓑ | Ⓒ | Ⓓ |
| 8. | $2^3 \cdot 2^4$ | $2^{12}$ | 8. | Ⓐ | Ⓑ | Ⓒ | Ⓓ |

9.   The number of students in a math class is 4 more than twice the number of students in a chemistry class. The chemistry class has $c$ students.

| | Column A | Column B | | | | | |
|---|---|---|---|---|---|---|---|
| | $2c + 4$ | The number of students in the math class | 9. | Ⓐ | Ⓑ | Ⓒ | Ⓓ |

10.   The price of a compact disk is $d$ dollars.

| | Column A | Column B | | | | | |
|---|---|---|---|---|---|---|---|
| | The compact disk at 20% off the list price | $0.20d$ dollars | 10. | Ⓐ | Ⓑ | Ⓒ | Ⓓ |

**Fill in the circle of the letter that corresponds to the correct answer.**

1. Which integer is between $-\frac{33}{4}$ and $-\frac{22}{3}$?

    **A.** 8    **B.** 7    **C.** $-7$    **D.** $-8$    **E.** $-11$

    1. Ⓐ Ⓑ Ⓒ Ⓓ Ⓔ

2. The symbol $\circ$ represents one of the four basic operations of arithmetic. It has the following properties: If $a$ and $b$ are real numbers, $a \circ b = -(b \circ a)$. If $a$ and $b$ are real numbers, $0 \circ a = -a$. Which operation(s) must $\circ$ represent?

    **A.** $+$ or $-$    **B.** $-$ only    **C.** $+$ only    **D.** $\times$ only    **E.** $\div$ only

    2. Ⓐ Ⓑ Ⓒ Ⓓ Ⓔ

3. Expressed as a sum, $7 - (-6) - 4 - (-3) = \boxed{\quad ? \quad}$

    **A.** $7 + 6 + 4 + (-3)$    **B.** $7 + (-6) + (-4) + 3$
    **C.** $7 + (-6) + (-4) + (-3)$    **D.** $7 + 6 + (-4) + 3$
    **E.** $7 + 6 + (-4) + (-3)$

    3. Ⓐ Ⓑ Ⓒ Ⓓ Ⓔ

4. If $r = p + q$ and $s = 2p - q$, what is $r - s$ when $p = 2$ and $q = 3$?

    **A.** 12    **B.** 4    **C.** 2    **D.** $-2$    **E.** $-4$

    4. Ⓐ Ⓑ Ⓒ Ⓓ Ⓔ

5. Arrange in increasing order:

    I. $-4$    II. $-\frac{27}{6}$    III. $-3.9$    IV. $-\frac{7}{2}$.

    **A.** IV, III, I, II    **B.** II, I, IV, III    **C.** II, I, III, IV
    **D.** I, II, III, IV    **E.** III, IV, I, II

    5. Ⓐ Ⓑ Ⓒ Ⓓ Ⓔ

6. What is the value of $|x| - |y| - 2$ when $x = -7$ and $y = 3$?

    **A.** $-12$    **B.** $-6$    **C.** 2    **D.** 6    **E.** 8

    6. Ⓐ Ⓑ Ⓒ Ⓓ Ⓔ

7. Which is the closest estimate to $3.9 + 2(5.2) - 6.3 \div 3$?

    **A.** $-5$    **B.** 8    **C.** 12    **D.** 13    **E.** 16

    7. Ⓐ Ⓑ Ⓒ Ⓓ Ⓔ

8. The expression $4(x + 4) - 3(3 - x)$ can be simplified to $\boxed{\quad ? \quad}$.

    **A.** $13x + 25$    **B.** $13x - 7$    **C.** $7x + 16$
    **D.** $7x + 7$    **E.** $7x - 7$

    8. Ⓐ Ⓑ Ⓒ Ⓓ Ⓔ

9. What is the product of $\frac{3}{8}$ and $\frac{4}{3}$?

    **A.** $\frac{1}{6}$    **B.** $\frac{9}{32}$    **C.** $\frac{1}{2}$    **D.** $\frac{41}{24}$    **E.** $\frac{32}{9}$

    9. Ⓐ Ⓑ Ⓒ Ⓓ Ⓔ

Solve the problem and write your answer at the top of the grid on the
separate answer sheet. Then fill in the corresponding ellipses in the answer
grid. (Your answer can be an integer, a decimal number, or a fraction.)

1. What is the value of $3 - 2(1 - x)$ when $x = 4$?

2. Jolene entered a glass-enclosed elevator on the first floor of her hotel. She stayed on the
   elevator to watch the view while the elevator went up 15 floors, down 3 floors, and up 6 floors.
   How many floors will she go down if she presses the elevator button for the 8th floor?

3. You paid $13.68 for 12 gallons of gasoline. What was the price per gallon, in dollars?

4. An $8 book is marked 10% off, but there is a 5% sales tax on the purchase price. What would
   a customer pay in dollars to buy this book?

5. The sum of two consecutive odd numbers is 28. What is the product of these two numbers?

6. A rectangular box has inside dimensions of 9 centimeters by 12 centimeters by 6 centimeters.
   The box is filled with cubical blocks whose sides are 3 centimeters. How many blocks does it
   take to completely fill the box?

7. What is the value of $4r^4$ if $r = -2$?

8. The average of three numbers is 9. The sum of the first two numbers is 17. What is the third
   number?

**In 9–12, use the table which shows the inventory
of T-shirts at a gift shop.**

|         | Red | White | Blue |
|---------|-----|-------|------|
| Small   | 5   | 8     | 6    |
| Medium  | 12  | 24    | 8    |
| Large   | 17  | 20    | 16   |
| X-Large | 11  | 23    | 10   |

9. What is the total number of white T-shirts?

10. What is the total number of small and medium T-shirts?

11. What fraction of the total inventory are the large blue T-shirts?

12. A customer buys 1 small blue T-shirt, 2 medium red T-shirts, 3 medium white T-shirts, 4 large
    red T-shirts, and 3 x-large blue T-shirts. How many blue T-shirts are left in the inventory?

**Fill in the circle of the letter that corresponds to the correct answer.**

1. Let $4s + 2 = -6$, then $s^2 + 3 = $ [ ? ]

    **A.** $-1$     **B.** $2\frac{1}{2}$     **C.** $3\frac{1}{4}$     **D.** $5$     **E.** $7$

    1.  Ⓐ  Ⓑ  Ⓒ  Ⓓ  Ⓔ

2. If $3x + 7 = 1$, then $|x| = $ [ ? ]

    **A.** $-2$     **B.** $-\frac{1}{2}$     **C.** $\frac{1}{3}$     **D.** $\frac{1}{2}$     **E.** $2$

    2.  Ⓐ  Ⓑ  Ⓒ  Ⓓ  Ⓔ

3. If $P = 2W + 2L$, then $L = $ [ ? ]

    **A.** $P - 2W$     **B.** $\frac{2W - P}{2}$     **C.** $\frac{P - 2W}{2}$
    **D.** $2W - P$     **E.** $\frac{P + 2W}{2}$

    3.  Ⓐ  Ⓑ  Ⓒ  Ⓓ  Ⓔ

4. Larry's math scores are 96, 92, 90, and 88. What must he score on the next test to have an average score of 92?

    **A.** $98$     **B.** $94$     **C.** $93.5$     **D.** $92$     **E.** $90$

    4.  Ⓐ  Ⓑ  Ⓒ  Ⓓ  Ⓔ

5. A bucket being filled with water is $\frac{3}{8}$ full after 60 seconds. How many more seconds will it take to fill the bucket?

    **A.** $160$     **B.** $132.5$     **C.** $100$     **D.** $80$     **E.** $22.5$

    5.  Ⓐ  Ⓑ  Ⓒ  Ⓓ  Ⓔ

6. A lawn-and-garden dealer wants to make a new blend of grass seed by using 200 pounds of $0.45 per pound seed and some $0.65 per pound seed. How much of the $0.65 seed does the dealer need to make a $0.55 per pound blend?

    **A.** $60$     **B.** $150$     **C.** $200$     **D.** $300$     **E.** $450$

    6.  Ⓐ  Ⓑ  Ⓒ  Ⓓ  Ⓔ

7. The average of three numbers is 8. If one of the three numbers is 12, what is the product of the other two numbers?

    **A.** $11$     **B.** $12$     **C.** $32$     **D.** $36$
    **E.** Can't be determined from the given information.

    7.  Ⓐ  Ⓑ  Ⓒ  Ⓓ  Ⓔ

8. What is the average of the expressions $4n + 3,\ 7n - 5,\ 3n + 7,\ $ and $2n - 1$?

    **A.** $8n - 2$     **B.** $4n + 4$     **C.** $16n$     **D.** $16n - 4$     **E.** $4n + 1$

    8.  Ⓐ  Ⓑ  Ⓒ  Ⓓ  Ⓔ

9. For all $x$, $3x - (-2)(4x - 3) + x(7 - x) = $ [ ? ]

    **A.** $6 + 2x - x^2$     **B.** $-9 + 11x - x^2$     **C.** $6 + 18x - x^2$
    **D.** $-6 + 18x - x^2$     **E.** $-6 + 6x - x^2$

    9.  Ⓐ  Ⓑ  Ⓒ  Ⓓ  Ⓔ

10. If $-4$ is a solution to $x^2 + bx - 36 = 0$, what is the value of $b$?

    **A.** $-13$     **B.** $-9$     **C.** $-5$     **D.** $5$     **E.** $9$

    10.  Ⓐ  Ⓑ  Ⓒ  Ⓓ  Ⓔ

If Column A is greater than Column B, fill in the circle for A.
If Column B is greater than Column A, fill in the circle for B.
If Column A is equal to Column B, fill in the circle for C.
If there is not enough information, fill in the circle for D.
Information centered between the columns concerns the quantities in both columns.

|  | Column A | Column B |  |
|---|---|---|---|

**1.** $3x - 6 = 12$

$x$                     6
**1.** Ⓐ Ⓑ Ⓒ Ⓓ

**2.** $4a + 7 = a - 2$

$-2$                 $a$
**2.** Ⓐ Ⓑ Ⓒ Ⓓ

In 3 and 4, refer to the information below.

**3.** $p > 0, \; q < 0$

$p + q$            $p - q$
**3.** Ⓐ Ⓑ Ⓒ Ⓓ

**4.** $pq$           $-\frac{p}{q}$
**4.** Ⓐ Ⓑ Ⓒ Ⓓ

**5.** $a = 2, \; b = 3, \; c = 6$

$a(b - c)$         $ab - ac$
**5.** Ⓐ Ⓑ Ⓒ Ⓓ

**6.** A triangle has three angles whose degree measures are
$a, b$, and $c$.

$a + b$            $c$
**6.** Ⓐ Ⓑ Ⓒ Ⓓ

**7.** $r = -4, \; s = 2$

$rs$               $-r$
**7.** Ⓐ Ⓑ Ⓒ Ⓓ

**8.** $p = 3 - 2q + 1 + q - 5 + 2q + 3 - q$

$p$                1
**8.** Ⓐ Ⓑ Ⓒ Ⓓ

**9.** $x > y > z > 0$

$x - z$          $y - z$
**9.** Ⓐ Ⓑ Ⓒ Ⓓ

**10.** $(6 - W)v = 2v = 8$

$W$               $v$
**10.** Ⓐ Ⓑ Ⓒ Ⓓ

**Fill in the circle of the letter that corresponds to the correct answer.**

**1.** What is the slope of the line $3x - y = 6$?

    **A.** $-6$    **B.** $-3$    **C.** $1$    **D.** $2$    **E.** $3$

1. Ⓐ Ⓑ Ⓒ Ⓓ Ⓔ

**2.** What is the $y$-intercept of the line $-2x + y = 4$?

    **A.** $4$    **B.** $2$    **C.** $1$    **D.** $-2$    **E.** $-4$

2. Ⓐ Ⓑ Ⓒ Ⓓ Ⓔ

**3.** Which equation below represents $4x + 3y = -12$ in slope-intercept form?

    **A.** $y = -4x - 12$    **B.** $y = -\frac{4}{3}x - 4$    **C.** $y = \frac{4}{3}x + 4$
    **D.** $y = \frac{3}{4}x - 4$      **E.** $y = \frac{4}{3}x - 4$

3. Ⓐ Ⓑ Ⓒ Ⓓ Ⓔ

**4.** Line $l$ is graphed on a standard $(x, y)$ coordinate plane. What is the slope of line $l$?

4. Ⓐ Ⓑ Ⓒ Ⓓ Ⓔ

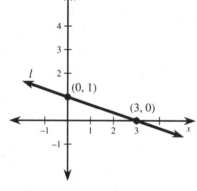

    **A.** $-3$
    **B.** $-2$
    **C.** $-\frac{1}{3}$
    **D.** $\frac{1}{3}$
    **E.** $3$

**5.** Which of the following equations represent the graph shown below?

5. Ⓐ Ⓑ Ⓒ Ⓓ Ⓔ

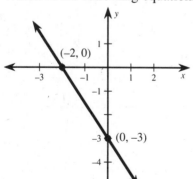

    **A.** $3x - 2y = -6$
    **B.** $-3x + 2y = 6$
    **C.** $3x - 2y = 6$
    **D.** $3x + 2y = -6$
    **E.** $3x + 2y = 6$

**6.** What is the sum of the two solutions for $x$ in the equation $|x + 2| - 4 = -3$?

6. Ⓐ Ⓑ Ⓒ Ⓓ Ⓔ

    **A.** $-4$    **B.** $-2$    **C.** $0$    **D.** $2$    **E.** $4$

Solve the problem and write your answer at the top of the grid on the
separate answer sheet. Then fill in the corresponding ellipses in the answer
grid. (Your answer can be an integer, a decimal number, or a fraction.)

1. What is the slope of the line containing the points
   $(-1, -3)$ and $(2, 1)$?

2. What is the $y$-intercept of the graph of the line
   $3x + 2y = 4$?

3. What is the slope of the line parallel to
   $3.2x - 2y = 2.9$?

**In 4 and 5, use the graph below. The coordinates of the points have integer
values.**

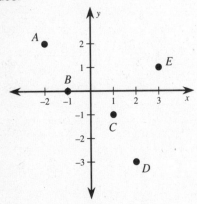

4. What is the value of the $x$-coordinate of point $C$?

5. What is the value of the $y$-coordinate of point $E$?

6. A rectangle has vertices at $(-3, 4)$, $(-3, -2)$, and $(2, -2)$. What is the $x$-coordinate of the
   fourth vertex?

7. A right triangle has vertices at $(2, 1)$ and $(6, 1)$. What is a possible $x$-coordinate value of the
   third vertex?

8. A third-grade class is attempting to collect one million pull tabs from soda cans. At the end of
   the 2nd week 3000 tabs had been collected. After 5 weeks there was a total of 4500 tabs. What
   was the average rate of increase per week of tabs?

9. Grid in one possible value for the solution to $|x - 7| = 4$.

10. Grid in one possible value for the solution to $|x - 5| + 6 = 10$.

Fill in the circle of the letter that corresponds to the correct answer.

1. What is the equation of a line with the same slope as the line
   $y = 3x - 2$ and a $y$-intercept of $-\frac{1}{2}$?

   **A.** $y = -2x - \frac{1}{2}$    **B.** $y = -2x + \frac{1}{2}$    **C.** $y = 3x - \frac{1}{2}$
   **D.** $y = 3x + \frac{1}{2}$    **E.** $y = -3x + \frac{1}{2}$

   1. Ⓐ Ⓑ Ⓒ Ⓓ Ⓔ

2. What is the equation of a line that contains the points $(-5, \ 4)$ and
   $(2, \ 1)$?

   **A.** $-7x + 3y = 17$    **B.** $-3x + 7y = 13$    **C.** $3x - 7y = 13$
   **D.** $3x + 7y = 13$    **E.** $7x + 3y = 17$

   2. Ⓐ Ⓑ Ⓒ Ⓓ Ⓔ

3. A line passes through the points $(4, \ p)$ and $(-2, \ -p)$ and has a
   slope of $\frac{1}{3}$. What is the value of $p$?

   **A.** $-1$    **B.** $-\frac{1}{3}$    **C.** $0$    **D.** $\frac{1}{3}$    **E.** $1$

   3. Ⓐ Ⓑ Ⓒ Ⓓ Ⓔ

4. A line with a slope of $-2$ goes through the point $(3, 2)$. If $(-3, \ k)$
   is another point on the line, what is the value of $k$?

   **A.** $2$    **B.** $5$    **C.** $\frac{11}{2}$    **D.** $13$    **E.** $14$

   4. Ⓐ Ⓑ Ⓒ Ⓓ Ⓔ

5. Using the graph below, which statement is true about the slopes $m_1$
   and $m_2$ of lines $l_1$ and $l_2$, respectively?

   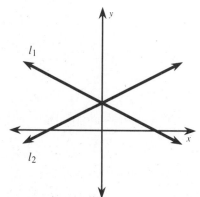

   **A.** $m_1 + m_2 < 0$
   **B.** $m_1 \cdot m_2 < 0$
   **C.** $m_1 \cdot m_2 > 0$
   **D.** $m_1 = \frac{1}{2}m_2$
   **E.** $m_1 = \frac{1}{m_2}$

   5. Ⓐ Ⓑ Ⓒ Ⓓ Ⓔ

6. A driver was fined $20.00 plus $4.00 for every mile per hour over
   the speed limit of 55 mph. If the fine was $76.00, how fast was the
   driver going?

   **A.** $14$    **B.** $19$    **C.** $64$    **D.** $69$    **E.** $74$

   6. Ⓐ Ⓑ Ⓒ Ⓓ Ⓔ

If Column A is greater than Column B, fill in the circle for A.
If Column B is greater than Column A, fill in the circle for B.
If Column A is equal to Column B, fill in the circle for C.
If there is not enough information, fill in the circle for D.
Information centered between the columns concerns the quantities in both columns.

| <u>Column A</u> | <u>Column B</u> | |
|---|---|---|

**1.**    Rachael has saved $40 to buy a $160 compact disk player.          **1.**  Ⓐ  Ⓑ  Ⓒ  Ⓓ
           She saves $10 a week by babysitting.

The number of weeks Rachael                    14
   must save to buy the
   compact disk player

---

**2.**    A long distance call between City $X$ and City $Y$ costs          **2.**  Ⓐ  Ⓑ  Ⓒ  Ⓓ
           $0.60 for the first minute and $0.30 for each additional
           minute.
                $4.00                The cost of a 7-minute call from
                                        City $X$ to City $Y$

---

**Questions 3 and 4 refer to the following graph.**

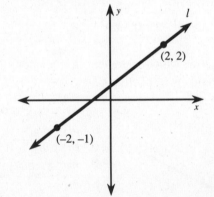

---

**3.**        The slope of line $l$                    1                    **3.**  Ⓐ  Ⓑ  Ⓒ  Ⓓ

---

**4.**        The $y$-intercept of line $l$             $\frac{1}{2}$        **4.**  Ⓐ  Ⓑ  Ⓒ  Ⓓ

---

**5.**                      $3x + 2y = -4$                                   **5.**  Ⓐ  Ⓑ  Ⓒ  Ⓓ

            The slope of the line      The $y$-intercept of the line

---

**6.**  The slope of a line containing          2                          **6.**  Ⓐ  Ⓑ  Ⓒ  Ⓓ
            the point $(3, -1)$

**Fill in the circle of the letter that corresponds to the correct answer.**

1. If $n$ is an integer and $0 < 4n < 10$, what are all the possible integer values of $n$?

    **1.**  Ⓐ  Ⓑ  Ⓒ  Ⓓ  Ⓔ

    **A.** 0 only      **B.** 1 only      **C.** 2 only
    **D.** 0 and 1 only      **E.** 1 and 2 only

2. If $p > q > 0$, then which expression is less than 0?

    **2.**  Ⓐ  Ⓑ  Ⓒ  Ⓓ  Ⓔ

    **A.** $p + q$    **B.** $p - q$    **C.** $q - p$    **D.** $pq$
    **E.** Not enough given information

3. Which graph represents the solution for $3x - 2(3 - x) \geq 4$?

    **3.**  Ⓐ  Ⓑ  Ⓒ  Ⓓ  Ⓔ

    **A.**

    **B.**

    **C.**

    **D.**

    **E.**

4. For all positive values of $x$, $y$, and $z$, with $z > y$ and $z < x$, which of the following must be true?

    **4.**  Ⓐ  Ⓑ  Ⓒ  Ⓓ  Ⓔ

    I. $y < z + x$    II. $y < 2x$    III. $y + z < x$

    **A.** I. only      **B.** II. only      **C.** I. and II. only
    **D.** II. and III. only      **E.** I., II., and III.

5. For which values of $x$ is the inequality $2(2x + 3) \geq 5x + 8$ true?

    **5.**  Ⓐ  Ⓑ  Ⓒ  Ⓓ  Ⓔ

    **A.** $x \leq -2$    **B.** $x \leq -1$    **C.** $x \geq -2$
    **D.** $x \geq -1$    **E.** $x \geq 2$

6. You live 2 miles from school and your study partner lives 1 mile from you. Which inequality describes the possible distances between school and your study partner's home?

    **6.**  Ⓐ  Ⓑ  Ⓒ  Ⓓ  Ⓔ

    **A.** $0 \leq x \leq 1$    **B.** $0 \leq x \leq 2$    **C.** $0 \leq x \leq 3$
    **D.** $1 \leq x \leq 2$    **E.** $1 \leq x \leq 3$

7. Which point is not a solution of $y < x + 1$?

    **7.**  Ⓐ  Ⓑ  Ⓒ  Ⓓ  Ⓔ

    **A.** $(-2, 2)$    **B.** $(-2, -2)$    **C.** $(2, -2)$
    **D.** $(2, 1)$    **E.** $(-1, -3)$

Solve the problem and write your answer at the top of the grid on the
separate answer sheet. Then fill in the corresponding ellipses in the answer
grid. (Your answer can be an integer, a decimal number, or a fraction.)

1. Grid in one possible value of $x$ that is a solution for
   $3x + 2 > x + 4$.

2. If $x = -3$, what is one possible value for $y$ when
   $y \geq -3x + 1$?

3. Grid in one of the endpoints of the graph $|3x - 4| \leq 2$.

4. Grid in a possible solution for $24 - 2x \geq 4$.

5. Fay and Helen participated in a 3-mile walk. Fay finished ahead of Helen, and Helen's time for
   the walk was 45 minutes. What was Fay's average rate, $r$, in miles per minute?

6. The temperature in City A during January ranges from 0°F to 60°F. The temperature in July
   ranges from 48°F to 100°F. Grid in one possible temperature that could occur in both January
   and July.

7. A large pizza costs $7 plus $0.75 for each additional topping. If $12 is to be spent on pizza,
   what is the greatest number of additional toppings that could be on the pizza?

8. The inequality $2x - 4y \geq 3$ separates the coordinate plane into two half planes. What is the
   slope of the line separating the half planes?

**In 9 and 10, use the pie graph.**

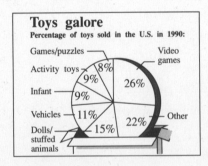

Toys galore
Percentage of toys sold in the U.S. in 1990:

Games/puzzles — Video games
Activity toys — 8%
9%
Infant — 9%
26%
Vehicles — 11%
Dolls/ stuffed animals — 15%
22% — Other

9. Of 5000 toys sold in 1990, how many were video games?

10. Of 5000 toys sold in 1990, how many were either games, puzzles, or activity toys?

**Fill in the circle of the letter that corresponds to the correct answer.**

1. If $x$ is 3 less than the product of $y$ and 6, and if $y = -1$, then what is the value of $x$?

   A. $-9$     B. $-3$     C. 2     D. 8
   E. Not enough information given

   1. (A) (B) (C) (D) (E)

2. If $5x = 3y = 30$, then $x + y = \boxed{?}$

   A. 15     B. 16     C. 18     D. 50     E. 60

   2. (A) (B) (C) (D) (E)

3. If $x + y = 7$ and $x - y = 3$, then $xy = \boxed{?}$

   A. 21     B. 20     C. 15     D. 10     E. 5

   3. (A) (B) (C) (D) (E)

4.

   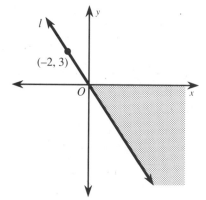

   (−2, 3)

   Which one of the following points is located in the shaded region in the graph above?

   A. $(-2, -3)$     B. $(4, 3)$     C. $(4, -7)$
   D. $(5, -8)$     E. $(6, -8)$

   4. (A) (B) (C) (D) (E)

5. A person paid $15 for greeting cards priced at $1 and $2 each. If the person purchased three $1-greeting cards for every $2-greeting card, what was the total number of greeting cards purchased?

   A. 13     B. 12     C. 11     D. 10     E. 9

   5. (A) (B) (C) (D) (E)

6. If $y = 3x + 2$, then $-4y = \boxed{?}$

   A. $-12x - 8$     B. $-12x + 2$     C. $-3x - 8$
   D. $3x - 8$     E. $12x + 8$

   6. (A) (B) (C) (D) (E)

7. If $y - 3 = 7$ and $x + 3y = 6$, then $x = \boxed{?}$

   A. 36     B. 18     C. 10     D. $-6$     E. $-24$

   7. (A) (B) (C) (D) (E)

8. If $x - 3y = 20$ and $3x + y = 20$, then $x + y = \boxed{?}$

   A. $-8$     B. $-4$     C. 4     D. 8     E. 12

   8. (A) (B) (C) (D) (E)

If Column A is greater than Column B, fill in the circle for A.
If Column B is greater than Column A, fill in the circle for B.
If Column A is equal to Column B, fill in the circle for C.
If there is not enough information, fill in the circle for D.
Information centered between the columns concerns the quantities in both columns.

| Column A | Column B | |
|---|---|---|

**1.** $4y - 2x = 14$

$2y - x$ ............................................ $8$ 　　　1.  Ⓐ Ⓑ Ⓒ Ⓓ

**2.** $2x + y = 5$
$y = -1$

$x$ ............................................ $3$ 　　　2.  Ⓐ Ⓑ Ⓒ Ⓓ

**3.** $x = \frac{4}{3}y$ and $x = 5 - 2y$

$2$ ............................................ $y$ 　　　3.  Ⓐ Ⓑ Ⓒ Ⓓ

**4.** $x + y = 2$
$x - y = 7$

$x$ ............................................ $4$ 　　　4.  Ⓐ Ⓑ Ⓒ Ⓓ

**5.** $x - y > 2$
$x + y < 2$

$y$ ............................................ $2$ 　　　5.  Ⓐ Ⓑ Ⓒ Ⓓ

**6.** $a + b = c$
$abc \neq 0$

$a + b$ 　　The average (arithmetic mean) of $a$, $b$, and $c$ 　　　6.  Ⓐ Ⓑ Ⓒ Ⓓ

**7.** $3x + 2y = 5$ and $x - 2y = 7$

$x - y$ ............................................ $x + y$ 　　　7.  Ⓐ Ⓑ Ⓒ Ⓓ

**8.** $2x + y = a$ and $-x + y = 2a$

$x$ ............................................ $y$ 　　　8.  Ⓐ Ⓑ Ⓒ Ⓓ

**9.** Your teacher is giving a 100-point exam. There is a total of 16 questions, each worth either 5 or 10 points. 　　　9.  Ⓐ Ⓑ Ⓒ Ⓓ

The number of 10-point questions 　　The number of 5-point questions

**Fill in the circle of the letter that corresponds to the correct answer.**

1. Which of the following is equal to $3^3 \cdot 3^2$?

   **A.** $9^6$    **B.** $9^5$    **C.** $3^9$    **D.** $3^6$    **E.** $3^5$

   1.  Ⓐ  Ⓑ  Ⓒ  Ⓓ  Ⓔ

2. Which of the following is not equivalent to $5 \times 2^6$?
   I. $10 \times 2^5$    II. $20 \times 2^4$    III. $5^2 \times 2^5$

   **A.** I. only    **B.** II. only    **C.** III. only
   **D.** I. and II. only    **E.** II. and III. only

   2.  Ⓐ  Ⓑ  Ⓒ  Ⓓ  Ⓔ

3. What is the average (arithmetic mean) of $1^2$, $2^2$, and $3^2$?

   **A.** 4    **B.** $4\frac{2}{3}$    **C.** 5    **D.** 7    **E.** $10\frac{2}{3}$

   3.  Ⓐ  Ⓑ  Ⓒ  Ⓓ  Ⓔ

4. Which of the following is equivalent to $\frac{3x^2 y^0}{x^{-2} y^2}$?

   **A.** $3y^2$    **B.** $\frac{3}{y^2}$    **C.** $\frac{3x^4}{y^2}$    **D.** $\frac{3x^4}{y^{-2}}$    **E.** $\frac{3}{x^4 y^2}$

   4.  Ⓐ  Ⓑ  Ⓒ  Ⓓ  Ⓔ

5. Which of the following is equivalent to
   $3a^2 b^0 c^{-1} \cdot 2^2 ab^{-1} c^2 \cdot b^2 a^{-2}$?

   **A.** $6abc$    **B.** $6a^5 bc^2$    **C.** $12a^{-4} c^{-2}$
   **D.** $12ab^{-2} c^4$    **E.** $12abc$

   5.  Ⓐ  Ⓑ  Ⓒ  Ⓓ  Ⓔ

6. In scientific notation, $3000 + 250{,}000 = \boxed{\phantom{?}}$

   **A.** $2.53 \times 10^{10}$    **B.** $2.80 \times 10^7$    **C.** $2.53 \times 10^7$
   **D.** $2.80 \times 10^5$    **E.** $2.53 \times 10^5$

   6.  Ⓐ  Ⓑ  Ⓒ  Ⓓ  Ⓔ

7. $(6.2 \times 10^6) \div (3.1 \times 10^2) = \boxed{\phantom{?}}$

   **A.** $2.0 \times 10^8$    **B.** $3.1 \times 10^4$    **C.** $2.0 \times 10^4$
   **D.** $3.1 \times 10^3$    **E.** $2.0 \times 10^3$

   7.  Ⓐ  Ⓑ  Ⓒ  Ⓓ  Ⓔ

8. If $x$ is a positive number, then $(2^x)^2 \cdot 2^x = \boxed{\phantom{?}}$

   **A.** $2^{2x+2}$    **B.** $2^{3x}$    **C.** $2^{x^3}$    **D.** $4^{3x}$    **E.** $8^{3x}$

   8.  Ⓐ  Ⓑ  Ⓒ  Ⓓ  Ⓔ

9. If $x^2 > y^2$, which of the following could be values of
   $x$ and $y$?

   **A.** $x = 2$, $y = -3$    **B.** $x = \frac{1}{2}$, $y = -2$    **C.** $x = 0$, $y = -1$
   **D.** $x = -1$, $y = -2$    **E.** $x = -3$, $y = 2$

   9.  Ⓐ  Ⓑ  Ⓒ  Ⓓ  Ⓔ

10. The radius of a sphere is $1\frac{1}{2}$ meters. What is the volume of the
    sphere in cubic meters? (The volume of a sphere is $\frac{4}{3}\pi r^3$.)

    **A.** $2\pi$    **B.** $3\pi$    **C.** $\frac{9\pi}{2}$    **D.** $9\pi$    **E.** $18\pi$

    10.  Ⓐ  Ⓑ  Ⓒ  Ⓓ  Ⓔ

Solve the problem and write your answer at the top of the grid on the
separate answer sheet. Then fill in the corresponding ellipses in the answer
grid. (Your answer can be an integer, a decimal number, or a fraction.)

1. If $8 \times 10^t = 2 \times 40 \times 10^3$, what is the value of $t$?

2. If $4^{16} = (4^m)^2$, what is the value of $m$?

3. If $\frac{4^5 - 4^4}{3} = 4^x$, what is the value of $x$?

4. If $42,000 \times 10^3 = 4.2 \times 10^n$, what is the value of $n$?

5. If $(2.5 \times 10^4) \times (3.2 \times 10^2) = 8.0 \times 10^b$, what is the value of $b$?

6. In 1990 Americans spent 1.3 billion dollars on clothes for camping. The population of the United
   States in 1990 was 250 million. What was the average amount (in dollars) that Americans spent
   on camping clothes?

7. After memorizing 100 French words, a person starts to forget $\frac{1}{5}$ of the words each week. A
   model for this is $W = 100\left(\frac{4}{5}\right)^t$, where $W$ is the number of words remembered and $t$ is the
   number of weeks. How many words will this person remember after 2 weeks?

8. What does $\frac{5.6 \times 10^4}{1.4 \times 10^6}$ equal (in decimal notation)?

9. A ball has a diameter of 1 foot. A smaller ball has a diameter of $\frac{1}{2}$ foot. The volume of the
   larger ball is how many times as great as the volume of the smaller ball? (The volume of a
   sphere is $\frac{4}{3}\pi r^3$.)

10. What is the value of $4r^3 + 3t^2$ when $r = \frac{1}{2}$ and $t = -2$?

11. If $4.23 \times 10^6$ is written in decimal form, how many digits are in the number?

12. Let $\frac{x^2 y}{y^{-1}} \cdot \frac{3x^{-2} y^2}{4y^4} = \frac{3}{4}(xy)^m$.
    What is the value of $m$?

**Fill in the circle of the letter that corresponds to the correct answer.**

1. What is the value of $2x^2 - 3x + 5$ when $x = -1$?

    **A.** 0    **B.** 4    **C.** 6    **D.** 10    **E.** 12

    1. Ⓐ Ⓑ Ⓒ Ⓓ Ⓔ

2. If 2 is one solution to $-x^2 + bx - 8 = 0$, what is the value of $b$?

    **A.** $-6$    **B.** $-4$    **C.** 2    **D.** 4    **E.** 6

    2. Ⓐ Ⓑ Ⓒ Ⓓ Ⓔ

3. One leg of a right triangle has a length of 12 cm and the other leg has a length of 5 cm. What is the length of the hypotenuse?

    **A.** 169 cm    **B.** 49 cm    **C.** 17 cm
    **D.** $\sqrt{119}$ cm    **E.** 13 cm

    3. Ⓐ Ⓑ Ⓒ Ⓓ Ⓔ

4. If $n > 0$, what are the roots of $x^2 - nx - 12n^2 = 0$?

    **A.** $6n$ and $-2n$    **B.** $4n$ and $-3n$    **C.** $-4n$ and $3n$
    **D.** $-6n$ and $2n$    **E.** $-12n$ and $n$

    4. Ⓐ Ⓑ Ⓒ Ⓓ Ⓔ

5. A 10-foot ladder is placed against the windowsill of a house that is 8 feet above the ground. What is the approximate distance from the base of the house to the base of the ladder?

    **A.** 1 ft    **B.** 2 ft    **C.** 4 ft    **D.** 6 ft    **E.** 8 ft

    5. Ⓐ Ⓑ Ⓒ Ⓓ Ⓔ

6. Which set contains both solutions to $x^2 - 2x - 15 = 0$?

    **A.** $\{-3, 1, 5, 7\}$    **B.** $\{-7, -5, -3, -1\}$    **C.** $\{-7, -5, 1, 3\}$
    **D.** $\{1, 3, 5, 7\}$    **E.** $\{-5, -3, 1, 7\}$

    6. Ⓐ Ⓑ Ⓒ Ⓓ Ⓔ

7. If $a$ and $b$ are positive numbers and $a^2 + b^2 = 52$ and $a^2 - b^2 = 20$, what does $b$ equal?

    **A.** 2    **B.** 4    **C.** 6    **D.** 8    **E.** 10

    7. Ⓐ Ⓑ Ⓒ Ⓓ Ⓔ

8. If $r_1$ and $r_2$ are the radii of two circles, and if $2 \le r_1 \le 5$ and $3 \le r_2 \le 6$, what is the greatest possible difference between the areas of the circles?

    **A.** $32\pi$    **B.** $21\pi$    **C.** $16\pi$    **D.** $11\pi$    **E.** $4\pi$

    8. Ⓐ Ⓑ Ⓒ Ⓓ Ⓔ

9. Which of the following expressions represent the solutions for $x^2 - x - 6 < 0$?

    **A.** $x = -2$ and $x = 3$    **B.** $x < -2$ or $x > 3$    **C.** $-2 < x < 3$
    **D.** $x \le -2$ or $x \ge 3$    **E.** $-2 \le x \le 3$

    9. Ⓐ Ⓑ Ⓒ Ⓓ Ⓔ

If Column A is greater than Column B, fill in the circle for A.
If Column B is greater than Column A, fill in the circle for B.
If Column A is equal to Column B, fill in the circle for C.
If there is not enough information, fill in the circle for D.
Information centered between the columns concerns the quantities in both columns.

| | **Column A** | **Column B** | |
|---|---|---|---|

**1.** $13^2 - 12^2$        $5^2$     **1.** Ⓐ Ⓑ Ⓒ Ⓓ

---

**2.** $m > 0$ and $m^2 = n$     **2.** Ⓐ Ⓑ Ⓒ Ⓓ

     $1$           $n$

---

**3.** The formula for the volume of     **3.** Ⓐ Ⓑ Ⓒ Ⓓ
a cylinder is $V = \pi r^2 h$.

The radius of a cylinder with     The radius of a cylinder with

$V = 45$ and $h = 5$.        $V = 36$ and $h = 3$.

---

**4.** $a^2 - 4$         $a^2 - 9$     **4.** Ⓐ Ⓑ Ⓒ Ⓓ

---

**5.** $2n^2 - 4n - 7$      $7 + 4n - 2n^2$     **5.** Ⓐ Ⓑ Ⓒ Ⓓ

---

**6.** $x^2 - 9x + 20 = 0$     **6.** Ⓐ Ⓑ Ⓒ Ⓓ

     $3$           $x$

---

**7.** $y \le x^2 - 5x + 2$     **7.** Ⓐ Ⓑ Ⓒ Ⓓ

The greatest possible     The greatest possible
value of $y$ when         value of $y$ when
$x = -1$            $x = 1$

---

**8.** The number of solutions    The number of solutions     **8.** Ⓐ Ⓑ Ⓒ Ⓓ
for $x^2 + 5x + 1 = 0$      for $x^2 - 3x + 2 = 0$

---

**9.** A ball is thrown and follows a path modeled by     **9.** Ⓐ Ⓑ Ⓒ Ⓓ
$y = -0.03x^2 + 0.5x + 3$, where $y$ is the height of
the ball and $x$ is the horizontal distance
that the ball travels.

The height of the ball     The height of the ball
when $x = 10$         when $x = 20$

**Fill in the circle of the letter that corresponds to the correct answer.**

**1.** $(3x^3 + 2x^2 + x - 1) - (2x^3 + 3x - 5) = \boxed{\quad ? \quad}$

    **A.** $x^3 - 2x + 4$      **B.** $x^3 + 2x^2 - 4x - 6$
    **C.** $x^3 + 2x^2 - 4x - 4$      **D.** $x^3 + 2x^2 - 2x + 4$
    **E.** $x^3 + 2x^2 + 4x + 4$

    **1.** Ⓐ   Ⓑ   Ⓒ   Ⓓ   Ⓔ

**2.** $(-x^2 + 2) + (2x^2 - x + 1) = \boxed{\quad ? \quad}$

    **A.** $x^2 + x + 3$      **B.** $x^2 - x + 3$      **C.** $x^2 - x + 1$
    **D.** $x^2 - x - 1$      **E.** $-x^2 - x + 3$

    **2.** Ⓐ   Ⓑ   Ⓒ   Ⓓ   Ⓔ

**3.** $(3x + 2)(4x - 5) = \boxed{\quad ? \quad}$

    **A.** $12x^2 - 23x - 10$      **B.** $12x^2 - 15x - 10$
    **C.** $12x^2 - 7x - 10$      **D.** $12x^2 + 7x - 10$
    **E.** $12x^2 + 23x - 10$

    **3.** Ⓐ   Ⓑ   Ⓒ   Ⓓ   Ⓔ

**4.**

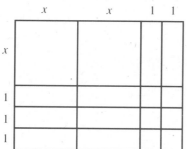

    **4.** Ⓐ   Ⓑ   Ⓒ   Ⓓ   Ⓔ

Which of the following expressions is represented by the model
shown above?

    **A.** $(2x + 2)(x + 3)$      **B.** $(x^2 + 2)(x + 3)$      **C.** $(2x^2 + 2)(x^2 + 3)$
    **D.** $3x^2 + 5x + 6$      **E.** $2x^2 + 5$

**5.** A banquet table has a length that is 3 feet less than 4
times its width. If $w$ represents the width, in feet, and
the total area of the table is 27 square feet, which of the
following equations could be used to determine the width?

    **A.** $27^2 - (4w - 3)^2 = w^2$      **B.** $w(4w + 3) = 27$
    **C.** $w(4w - 3) = 27$      **D.** $w(4w) - 3 = 27$
    **E.** $2w + 2(4w - 3) = 27$

    **5.** Ⓐ   Ⓑ   Ⓒ   Ⓓ   Ⓔ

**6.** If $x = -1$ is a solution to $x^2 + px - 5 = 0$, what is the value of $p$?

    **A.** 5     **B.** 4     **C.** 1     **D.** -1     **E.** -4

    **6.** Ⓐ   Ⓑ   Ⓒ   Ⓓ   Ⓔ

Solve the problem and write your answer at the top of the grid on the
separate answer sheet. Then fill in the corresponding ellipses in the answer
grid. (Your answer can be an integer, a decimal number, or a fraction.)

1. If $x^2 + y^2 = 34$ and $x^2 - y^2 = 16$, then for $y > 0$, $y = \boxed{\phantom{?}}$

2. If $x = -4$, then $(x + 3)^2 - 2x = \boxed{\phantom{?}}$

3. If $(a - 3)(a - c) = a^2 - 10a + 21$, then $c = \boxed{\phantom{?}}$

**In 4–6, use the following information.**

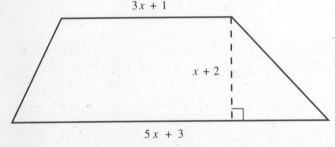

The formula for the area of a trapezoid is $A = \frac{1}{2}h(b_1 + b_2)$. Write the area of
the trapezoid above as a trinomial in terms of $x$.

4. What is the value of the leading coefficient of this trinomial?

5. What is the value of the constant term of this trinomial?

6. What is the area of the trapezoid when $x = 2$?

7. The area of the triangle below is 70 square inches. What is the length of its base in inches?
   (Area $= \frac{1}{2}bh$)

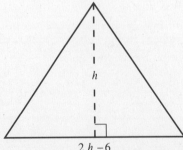

8. The volume of a certain rectangular box can be expressed as $2x^3 + 5x^2 + 3x$, where $x$ is an
   integer. The box has a volume of 108 cubic inches. What is the value of $x$?

**Fill in the circle of the letter that corresponds to the correct answer.**

1. Which of the following equals the ratio of $1\frac{1}{2}$ miles to 5 miles?

    A. $\frac{1}{5}$    B. $\frac{1}{7}$    C. $\frac{2}{5}$    D. $\frac{3}{7}$    E. $\frac{3}{10}$

    1. Ⓐ Ⓑ Ⓒ Ⓓ Ⓔ

2. A medium pizza will feed 8 small children or 3 adults. At this rate 5 medium pizzas will feed 24 small children and how many adults?

    A. 3    B. 4    C. 5    D. 6    E. 7

    2. Ⓐ Ⓑ Ⓒ Ⓓ Ⓔ

3. A $300-stereo system goes on sale for $225. The price was decreased by what percent?

    A. 25%    B. $33\frac{1}{3}\%$    C. 50%    D. $66\frac{2}{3}\%$    E. 75%

    3. Ⓐ Ⓑ Ⓒ Ⓓ Ⓔ

4. On one school day there were 21 students absent from school out of 280. What percent of students attended school that day?

    A. 7.5%    B. $\approx 8.1\%$    C. 75%    D. $\approx 91.9\%$
    E. 92.5%

    4. Ⓐ Ⓑ Ⓒ Ⓓ Ⓔ

5. Justin was paid $13.50 for 3 hours of work. How much did he receive for 11 hours of work?

    A. $33.00    B. $38.50    C. $42.50    D. $49.50
    E. $60.50

    5. Ⓐ Ⓑ Ⓒ Ⓓ Ⓔ

6. On the first day of your vacation you traveled 240 miles in 4 hours before stopping for lunch. You drove for 5 hours in the afternoon. If you traveled at the same rate in the afternoon as you did in the morning, how many miles did you travel on the first day?

    A. 600    B. 540    C. 480    D. 360    E. 300

    6. Ⓐ Ⓑ Ⓒ Ⓓ Ⓔ

7. For what values of $x$ is $\frac{(x+3)(x+1)}{(x+1)(x-1)}$ undefined?

    A. $-1$ only        B. 0 and $-1$ only    C. $-1$ and $-3$ only
    D. 1 and $-3$ only    E. 1 and $-1$ only

    7. Ⓐ Ⓑ Ⓒ Ⓓ Ⓔ

8. For all $n \neq 3$, $\frac{n^2-9}{n^2-3n} = \boxed{\phantom{?}}$

    A. $\frac{n+3}{n}$    B. $\frac{3}{n}$    C. 3    D. $n-1$    E. $9-3n$

    8. Ⓐ Ⓑ Ⓒ Ⓓ Ⓔ

9. A bag of marbles contains 6 red marbles, 8 white marbles, and 9 blue marbles. If you reach into the bag and randomly pick a marble, what is the probability that the marble is red?

    A. $\frac{6}{23}$    B. $\frac{8}{23}$    C. $\frac{6}{17}$    D. $\frac{9}{23}$    E. $\frac{17}{23}$

    9. Ⓐ Ⓑ Ⓒ Ⓓ Ⓔ

If Column A is greater than Column B, fill in the circle for A.
If Column B is greater than Column A, fill in the circle for B.
If Column A is equal to Column B, fill in the circle for C.
If there is not enough information, fill in the circle for D.
Information centered between the columns concerns the quantities in both columns.

|  | **Column A** | **Column B** |  |
|---|---|---|---|

**1.** $\frac{x}{3} = \frac{9}{27}$ and $\frac{4}{y} = \frac{12}{9}$

      $x$             $y$       **1.** Ⓐ Ⓑ Ⓒ Ⓓ

**2.** The ratio of 6 to 9 equals
the ratio of 2 to $\sqrt{x}$.

      $x$           3       **2.** Ⓐ Ⓑ Ⓒ Ⓓ

**3.** 4% of 20% of 20       2% of 40% of 20       **3.** Ⓐ Ⓑ Ⓒ Ⓓ

**4.** $6       The amount of interest earned
on $d$ dollars for 3 months
at 5% interest       **4.** Ⓐ Ⓑ Ⓒ Ⓓ

**5.** The ratio of tulips to daffodils
in a garden is 2 to 3.

The total number of       15       **5.** Ⓐ Ⓑ Ⓒ Ⓓ
tulips and daffodils

**6.** The cost per pound of     The cost per pound of       **6.** Ⓐ Ⓑ Ⓒ Ⓓ
fertilizer selling at       fertilizer selling at
$14.90 for 10 pounds     $7.90 for 5 pounds

**7.** $b > 0$

    $\frac{3}{b+\frac{1}{2}+\frac{1}{3}}$         3       **7.** Ⓐ Ⓑ Ⓒ Ⓓ

**8.** $x \neq 1$ and $x \neq 2$

    $\frac{3x^2-9x+6}{(x-1)(x-2)}$        3       **8.** Ⓐ Ⓑ Ⓒ Ⓓ

**9.** $p > q > 0$

    $p - q$         $\frac{p^2-q^2}{2(p+q)}$       **9.** Ⓐ Ⓑ Ⓒ Ⓓ

**Fill in the circle of the letter that corresponds to the correct answer.**

**1.** What is the value of the function $f(x) = -3x + 5$
when $x = -1$?

   **A.** 2   **B.** 4   **C.** 6   **D.** 7   **E.** 8

**1.**  Ⓐ  Ⓑ  ©  Ⓓ  Ⓔ

| Day | 1 | 2 | 3 | 4 |
|-----|------|------|------|------|
| Score | 20,000 | 20,500 | 21,000 | 21,500 |

**2.** Your high score each day for playing a new video game is listed in
the table above. If the same rate of increase continues, what will be
your high score on Day 9?

   **A.** 43,500   **B.** 26,500   **C.** 24,000
   **D.** 23,500   **E.** 23,000

**2.**  Ⓐ  Ⓑ  ©  Ⓓ  Ⓔ

**3.** What is the value of the function $f(a) = 2^a - 5$
when $a = 3$?

   **A.** −1   **B.** 1   **C.** 3   **D.** 5   **E.** 7

**3.**  Ⓐ  Ⓑ  ©  Ⓓ  Ⓔ

**4.** Which of the following is
a reflection in the $y$-axis
of the graph at the right?

**4.**  Ⓐ  Ⓑ  ©  Ⓓ  Ⓔ

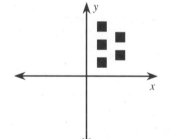

**A.**

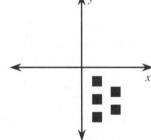

**B.**

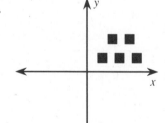

**C.**

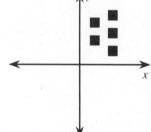

**D.**

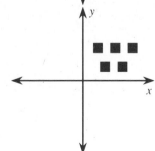

**E.**

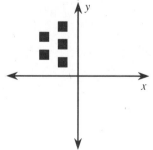

Solve the problem and write your answer at the top of the grid on the
separate answer sheet. Then fill in the corresponding ellipses in the answer
grid. (Your answer can be an integer, a decimal number, or a fraction.)

1. Grid in a value of $x$ that will give the function $f(x) = 20x - 15$ a value between 5 and 45.

2. Following the pattern established in the table,
   what is the value of the function when $x = 4$?

   | x | 0 | 1 | 2 | 3 | 4 |
   |---|---|---|---|---|---|
   | f(x) | 1 | 3 | 5 | 7 | ? |

3. When the function $f(x) = x^2 - 10x + 24$ is equal to 0, there are two possible values for $x$.
   What is one of the values of $x$?

4. The function $h(x) = x^2 + bx + 6$ is equal to 0 when $x = -2$. What is the value of $b$?

5. What is the value of the function $g(n) = 2^n + 1$ when $n = -2$?

6. For the function $f(x) = 3^x - 20$, what is the value of $x$ when $f(x) = 7$?

7. Determine the value of $a$ when the function $g(a) = \frac{1}{a} + 3$ is equal to 4.

8. Grid in one value of $p$ for which the function $f(p) = \frac{1}{p^2 - 6p + 8} - 2$ is undefined.

9. What is the value of the function $g(r) = \frac{1}{r^2 - 1}$ when $r = -2$?

**Hours Studied**

|         | Mon | Tues | Wed | Thur | Fri |
|---------|-----|------|-----|------|-----|
| **Kyra** | 2 | $2\frac{1}{2}$ | 1 | $1\frac{1}{2}$ | $\frac{1}{2}$ |
| **Caitlin** | $1\frac{1}{2}$ | 1 | $2\frac{1}{2}$ | $1\frac{1}{2}$ | 1 |

10. Kyra studied every day after school. What was the average number of hours per day that she
    studied?

**Fill in the circle of the letter that corresponds to the correct answer.**

**In 1 and 2, use the graph below.**

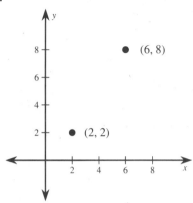

1. What is the distance between the points on the graph?

   **A.** $\sqrt{10}$    **B.** $2\sqrt{5}$    **C.** $2\sqrt{13}$    **D.** $2\sqrt{41}$    **E.** 14

   1.  Ⓐ Ⓑ Ⓒ Ⓓ Ⓔ

2. What is the midpoint of the line segment joining the two points?

   **A.** $(1, 3)$    **B.** $(2, 7)$    **C.** $(4, 5)$    **D.** $(5, 5)$    **E.** $(7, 2)$

   2.  Ⓐ Ⓑ Ⓒ Ⓓ Ⓔ

3. On a map with a coordinate plane, City $A$ is located at $(-2, 3)$ and City $B$ is located at $(4, -3)$. If each unit on the coordinate plane represents 100 miles, what is the approximate distance between City $A$ and City $B$?

   **A.** 849 miles    **B.** 632 miles    **C.** 600 miles
   **D.** 200 miles    **E.** 100 miles

   3.  Ⓐ Ⓑ Ⓒ Ⓓ Ⓔ

4. If $\sqrt[n]{48} = 2\sqrt[n]{6}$, then $n = \boxed{\phantom{?}}$

   **A.** 1    **B.** 2    **C.** 3    **D.** 4    **E.** 5

   4.  Ⓐ Ⓑ Ⓒ Ⓓ Ⓔ

5. $(\sqrt{5} - \sqrt{7})(\sqrt{7} - \sqrt{5}) = \boxed{\phantom{?}}$

   **A.** $-2$    **B.** $2\sqrt{35} - 12$    **C.** 2    **D.** $\sqrt{35} - 2$    **E.** $\sqrt{35} + 2$

   5.  Ⓐ Ⓑ Ⓒ Ⓓ Ⓔ

6. If the leg of a right triangle is 4 and the hypotenuse is 6, what is the length of the other leg?

   **A.** $2\sqrt{2}$    **B.** $2\sqrt{5}$    **C.** 4    **D.** 6    **E.** 8

   6.  Ⓐ Ⓑ Ⓒ Ⓓ Ⓔ

7. The area of a circle is $12\pi$ square meters. What is the circumference, in meters, of the circle?

   **A.** $2\sqrt{3}$    **B.** $4\sqrt{3}$    **C.** $2\pi\sqrt{3}$    **D.** $4\sqrt{3\pi}$    **E.** $4\pi\sqrt{3}$

   7.  Ⓐ Ⓑ Ⓒ Ⓓ Ⓔ

If Column A is greater than Column B, fill in the circle for A.
If Column B is greater than Column A, fill in the circle for B.
If Column A is equal to Column B, fill in the circle for C.
If there is not enough information, fill in the circle for D.
Information centered between the columns concerns the quantities in both columns.

<u>Column A</u>                          <u>Column B</u>

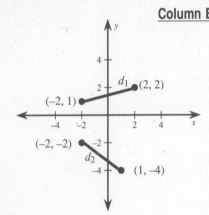

| | | | | |
|---|---|---|---|---|
| **1.** | Length of $d_1$ | Length of $d_2$ | **1.** | Ⓐ Ⓑ Ⓒ Ⓓ |

$$\sqrt{(x-1)^2 + (0-3)^2} = 5$$

| | | | | |
|---|---|---|---|---|
| **2.** | 4 | $x$ | **2.** | Ⓐ Ⓑ Ⓒ Ⓓ |
| **3.** | $\sqrt{45}$ | $3\sqrt{5}$ | **3.** | Ⓐ Ⓑ Ⓒ Ⓓ |
| **4.** | 2 | $\sqrt{27} - 2\sqrt{3}$ | **4.** | Ⓐ Ⓑ Ⓒ Ⓓ |

**5.**                    $a = \frac{1}{9}$                    **5.**  Ⓐ Ⓑ Ⓒ Ⓓ

$a - \sqrt{a}$                          0

**6.**  The ratio of 1 to 3 is equal to the ratio $\sqrt{b}$ to 27.     **6.**  Ⓐ Ⓑ Ⓒ Ⓓ

$b$                                9

**7.**                    $\frac{2}{p} = \frac{q}{8}$                    **7.**  Ⓐ Ⓑ Ⓒ Ⓓ

$pq$                               16

**8.**  The point $(x, y)$ is the midpoint of a line segment whose     **8.**  Ⓐ Ⓑ Ⓒ Ⓓ
endpoints are $(-3, -2)$ and $(4, 6)$.

$x$                                $y$

# Answers to Tests

■ **Mid-Chapter Test 1–A**

**1.** 52　**2.** 5　**3.** 55.9　**4.** 84　**5.** 0.6
**6.** 36　**7.** 19.63　**8.** $1.88　**9.** $3^4$
**10.** 8.9

■ **Mid-Chapter Test 1–B**

**1.** 165　**2.** 45　**3.** 101.1　**4.** 180
**5.** 60%　**6.** 360　**7.** 40.69　**8.** $1.97
**9.** $3^5$　**10.** 15.8

■ **Chapter Test 1–A**

**1.** 2.5　**2.** 4　**3.** 25.56　**4.** 58.7
**5.** $\frac{7x}{5}$ or $7x \div 5$　**6.** 16　**7.** 42.6
**8.** 23.07　**9.** 45.09　**10.** $x^3$　**11.** 9　**12.** 3
**13.** No　**14.** No　**15.** $5x - 3$
**16.** 10, plus the quotient of a number $x$ and 4.
(There are other correct phrases.)
**17.** $7 = 4B$　**18.** $3(n + 7) = 16$　**19.** 102
**20.** 10%, from 35% to 45%

■ **Chapter Test 1–B**

**1.** 2　**2.** 5　**3.** 13.70　**4.** 75.6
**5.** $7 - 5x$　**6.** 20　**7.** 61.2　**8.** 54.67
**9.** 59.22　**10.** $y^3$　**11.** 31　**12.** 5　**13.** Yes
**14.** Yes　**15.** $3x - 5$　**16.** The sum of 10 and
a number $x$, all divided by 4. (There are other
correct phrases.)　**17.** $7 < 4B$　**18.** $3n + 7 = 16$
**19.** 178　**20.** 10%, from 65% to 55%

■ **Chapter Test 1–C**

**1.** 3　**2.** 2.67　**3.** 2.06　**4.** 38.2　**5.** $\frac{7}{x+5}$
**6.** 17.5　**7.** 12.5, 25　**8.** 1.26　**9.** 161.87
**10.** $A^3$　**11.** 25　**12.** 44　**13.** Yes　**14.** No
**15.** $3(x - 5)$　**16.** Four divided by the sum of 10
and a number $x$. (There are other correct phrases.)
**17.** $7 \geq 4B$　**18.** $7 + 3n = 16$　**19.** 212
**20.** 40%

■ **Mid-Chapter Test 2–A**

**1.**
$-\frac{3}{2}$　　　　　　　3 is greater

-3 -2 -1 0 1 2 3

**2.** $-3, -\frac{1}{2}, 0, \frac{2}{3}, 1, 4$　**3.** $\frac{2}{3}$　**4.** 3.7
**5.** $-3$　**6.** $-3.23$　**7.** $\frac{7}{5}$　**8.** 2　**9.** No
**10.** $\begin{bmatrix} 9 & -1 & 1 \\ 4 & -2 & -3 \end{bmatrix}$

■ **Mid-Chapter Test 2–B**

**1.**
$\frac{3}{2}$　　　　$\frac{3}{2}$ is greater

-3 -2 -1 0 1 2 3

**2.** $-7, -3, 0, \frac{1}{2}, \frac{5}{4}, 2$　**3.** $-\frac{7}{3}$　**4.** 7.2
**5.** 2　**6.** $-5.34$　**7.** 3　**8.** $-7$　**9.** Yes
**10.** $\begin{bmatrix} -5 & -1 & 7 \\ 2 & 2 & -1 \end{bmatrix}$

■ **Chapter Test 2–A**

**1.** $-10, -\frac{5}{4}, 0, \frac{2}{3}, 1, \frac{3}{2}$
**2.**
$-2.5$　　$1.5$　　1.5 is greater.

-4 -3 -2 -1 0 1 2

**3.** $\frac{6}{5}$　**4.** $\frac{7}{3}$　**5.** 13.61　**6.** 0　**7.** 3
**8.** $\begin{bmatrix} -1 & 0 \\ -5 & 5 \\ 8 & -6 \end{bmatrix}$　**9.** $\begin{bmatrix} -6 & 6 \\ 9 & 3 \end{bmatrix}$　**10.** 80
**11.** 86.77　**12.** $68.75　**13.** 48　**14.** $79.75
**15.** $-x$　**16.** No　**17.** $60x - 40x^2$
**18.** $4x - 2$　**19.** A rate
**20.** 24.6 miles per gallon

■ **Chapter Test 2–B**

**1.** $-\frac{5}{6}, -\frac{1}{2}, 0, \frac{2}{3}, \frac{4}{5}, 7$
**2.**
$-1.5$　　$2.5$　　2.5 is greater.

-2 -1 0 1 2 3 4

**3.** $-\frac{6}{5}$　**4.** $-\frac{7}{3}$　**5.** 17.33　**6.** 7　**7.** 15
**8.** $\begin{bmatrix} -2 & 3 \\ 1 & 9 \\ -9 & 2 \end{bmatrix}$　**9.** $\begin{bmatrix} 7 & -10 \\ 12 & 4 \end{bmatrix}$
**10.** $-80$　**11.** $-82.56$　**12.** $115.50　**13.** $-26$
**14.** $88.20　**15.** $x - 5$
**16.** Yes　**17.** $51x^2 - 85x$
**18.** $5 - 3x$　**19.** A rate
**20.** 32.3 miles per gallon

■ **Chapter Test 2–C**

**1.** $\frac{2}{3}, \frac{1}{5}, 0, -\frac{2}{3}, -\frac{3}{2}, -\frac{5}{2}$
**2.**
$-2.5 -1.5$　　　$-1.5$ is greater.

-2 -2 -2 -1 0

**3.** $-\frac{6}{5}$　**4.** 0　**5.** 26.99　**6.** $3x - 14$
**7.** 10　**8.** $\begin{bmatrix} -5 & -5 \\ -5 & -5 \\ -5 & -5 \end{bmatrix}$　**9.** $\begin{bmatrix} 11 & -7 \\ 11 & -4 \end{bmatrix}$
**10.** $-160x^2$　**11.** 48.26　**12.** $101.76　**13.** 150
**14.** $90.10　**15.** $-x$　**16.** $23.24
**17.** $12x^2 - 3x^4$　**18.** $7 + 3x$　**19.** A ratio
**20.** 21.6 gallons

## Mid-Chapter Test 3–A

**1.** $\frac{7}{2}$  **2.** $-13$  **3.** $\frac{35}{8}$  **4.** $-\frac{1}{6}$
**5.** 26  **6.** $\frac{11}{2}$  **7.** 0  **8.** $\frac{7}{5}$
**9.** 4  **10.** $\frac{1}{5}$ hr or 12 min

## Mid-Chapter Test 3–B

**1.** $\frac{17}{4}$  **2.** 41  **3.** $\frac{1}{6}$  **4.** $\frac{5}{6}$  **5.** 19
**6.** $\frac{7}{2}$  **7.** $-\frac{1}{17}$  **8.** $\frac{23}{9}$  **9.** 5  **10.** 2 miles

## Chapter Test 3–A

**1.** 5  **2.** 15  **3.** 7  **4.** 17
**5.** $-5$  **6.** 4  **7.** $-1$  **8.** $\frac{5}{6}$
**9.** 2.35  **10.** $-0.15$  **11.** $t = \frac{3s-4}{5s}$
**12.** $m = \frac{n}{3-5n}$  **13.** 5  **14.** 2.55 in.
**15.** 34  **16.** $(3, 1), (-2, 2), (-1, -2)$
**17.**  **18.**

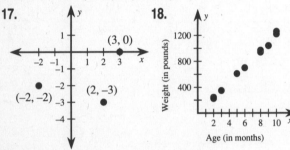

Weight tends to increase with age and the pattern of the points is approximately linear.

## Chapter Test 3–B

**1.** $\frac{11}{2}$  **2.** 56  **3.** $\frac{13}{4}$  **4.** 25
**5.** $-\frac{7}{6}$  **6.** 4  **7.** $-2$  **8.** $-\frac{7}{3}$
**9.** 2.19  **10.** $-0.71$  **11.** $t = \frac{2s-13}{7s}$
**12.** $m = \frac{5n}{4-6n}$  **13.** 6.6  **14.** 4.30 in.
**15.** 27  **16.** $(2, -3), (1, 4), (0, 3), (-2, 2)$

**17.**  **18.**

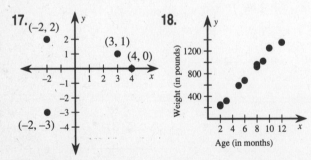

Weight tends to increase with age and the pattern of the points is approximately linear.

## Chapter Test 3–C

**1.** $-4$  **2.** $\frac{20}{3}$  **3.** 14  **4.** $\frac{26}{3}$  **5.** $-\frac{3}{7}$
**6.** $\frac{2}{3}$  **7.** $-\frac{5}{3}$  **8.** 10  **9.** 1.57
**10.** $-0.07$  **11.** $t = \frac{7s-12}{2s}$  **12.** $m = \frac{84}{5+2n}$

**13.** 1.6  **14.** 3.43 in.  **15.** 18
**16.** $(1, 3), (-3, 2), (3, 3), (-2, 4)$
**17.**  **18.**

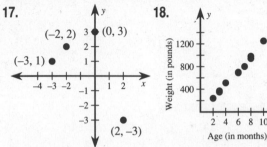

Weight tends to increase with age and the pattern of the points is approximately linear.

## Cumulative Test 1–3

**1.** 2.5  **2.** 45.84  **3.** 87.76  **4.** 56.8 in.
**5.** 41  **6.** $\frac{12x}{x+2}$  **7.** 267.51  **8.** 729
**9.** 80  **10.** 8  **11.** Yes  **12.** No
**13.** $3B \geq 10$  **14.** 38  **15.** 50%
**16.** $-\frac{7}{3}, -\frac{4}{5}, 0, \frac{1}{8}, \frac{3}{7}, \frac{5}{6}$  **17.** $-\frac{2}{3}$
**18.** $-1$  **19.** 29.22  **20.** $-4$  **21.** 20
**22.** $\begin{bmatrix} 10 & -1 & 7 \\ 8 & -2 & 8 \end{bmatrix}$  **23.** $\begin{bmatrix} 2 & -4 & -5 & 6 \\ 4 & 4 & -5 & 6 \end{bmatrix}$
**24.** $-492.64$  **25.** $850.50  **26.** 9
**27.** $x + 1$  **28.** No  **29.** $6 - 5x$
**30.** $\frac{1.93 \text{ lbs}}{1.80 \text{ lbs}}$  **31.** 25.1 gallons  **32.** 7
**33.** 6  **34.** $-9$  **35.** $-3$  **36.** 2.5
**37.** 0.72  **38.** 8  **39.** 31.83 in.$^2$  **40.** $R = \frac{2T}{3-10T}$
**41.** $(4, -1), (-3, 2), (-2, -2), (2, 3)$
**42.**

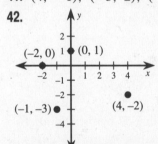

**43.** Approximately $152.4 billion
**44.** $4.7 billion profit on $80 billion revenue in 1987; $2.3 billion loss on $90 billion revenue in 1991.

## Mid-Chapter Test 4–A

**1.** $x = 2$  **2.** $y = -1$
**3.**

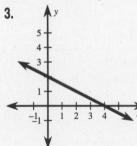

Points used may vary: (4, 0), (0, 2), (2, 1)

**4.** $(3, \frac{3}{2})$

**5.** $1.66 billion per year  **6.** Slope: $-3$

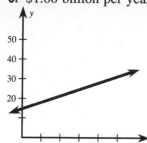

**7.** $7 per dozen

■ **Mid-Chapter Test 4–B**

**1.** $y = -3$    **2.** $x = 7$

**3.**

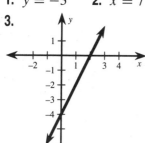

Points listed may vary: (2, 0), (0, −4), (1, −2)

**4.** $(\frac{2}{3}, 2)$

**5.** $2.19 billion per year  **6.** Slope: $-\frac{1}{5}$

**7.** 5 yds per minute

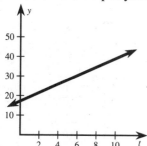

■ **Chapter Test 4–A**

**1.** $(-3, 4)$

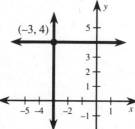

**2.** $x = 2$

**3.** $y = 7$

**4.** $(\frac{5}{2}, 3)$

**5.** $-\frac{11}{2}, -\frac{9}{2}, -4, -3, -2$

**6.** 4

**7.**

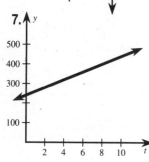

**8.** Slope: $\frac{9}{2}$

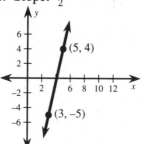

**9.** $\frac{7}{2}$ degrees per hour

**10.** Undefined    **11.** $285 per month    **12.** $y = \frac{4}{5}x$

**13.** Slope: $-7$;  $y$-intercept: (0, 15)

**14.** $y = \frac{5}{2}x - \frac{7}{2}$    **15.** $x = \frac{11}{5}$

**16.** $y = 4x - 2$    **17.** (3, 2)

**18.**

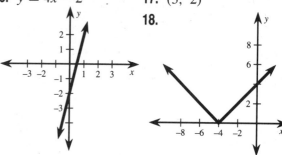

**19.** 11, −7

**20.** 100, 0; the maximum and minimum temperatures between which water is liquid

■ **Chapter Test 4–B**

**1.** $(-5, 3)$

**2.** $x = 7$

**3.** $y = 4$

**4.** $(\frac{3}{2}, 2)$

**5.** 2, 1, 0, −1, −2

**6.** −3

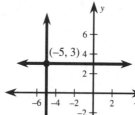

**7.**

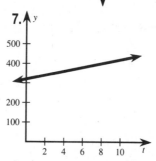

**8.** Slope: $-\frac{5}{8}$

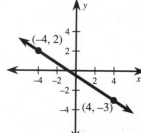

**9.** 11 degrees per hour

**10.** $\frac{1}{2}$    **11.** $317 per month    **12.** $y = -\frac{7}{2}x$

**13.** Slope: 7; $y$-intercept: −15

**14.** $y = \frac{8}{3}x - \frac{5}{3}$    **15.** $\frac{19}{11}$

**16.** $y = 3x - 2$    **17.** (4, −3)

**18.**

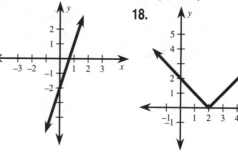

**19.** 8, −8

**20.** 184, 114; the maximum and minimum temperatures between which iodine is liquid

## Chapter Test 4–C

**1.** $(-2, -4)$

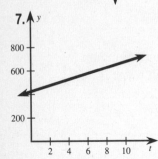

**2.** $y = -2$

**3.** $x = -5$

**4.** $\left(-\frac{3}{2}, 6\right)$

**5.** $6, \frac{17}{3}, 5, \frac{13}{3}, 4$

**6.** $x$-intercept: $-4$
$y$-intercept: $-3$

**7.**

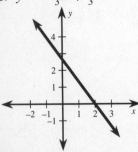

**8.** Slope: $\frac{7}{15}$

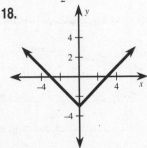

**9.** $-\frac{11}{3}$ degrees per hour

**10.** $-\frac{12}{17}$   **11.** \$1231 per month   **12.** $y = \frac{5}{4}x - 3$

**13.** Slope: $\frac{2}{5}$;  $y$-intercept: $-2$

**14.** $y = \frac{1}{6}x + \frac{1}{3}$   **15.** $\frac{13}{5}$

**16.** $y = -\frac{4}{3}x + \frac{8}{3}$   **17.** $\left(5, -\frac{1}{2}\right)$

**18.**

 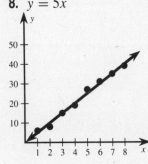

**19.** $x = 7, x = -1$

**20.** 79, –117; the maximum and minimum temperatures between which alcohol is liquid

### Mid-Chapter Test 5–A

**1.** $y = 5x - \frac{1}{2}$   **2.** $y = 2x - 2$

**3.** $y = 5x + 2.50$   **4.** $y = \frac{2}{3}x - \frac{14}{3}$

**5.** $y = 4x + 8$   **6.** $y = -x + 3$

**7.** $y = -\frac{1}{2}x - 2$   **8.** $y = 5x$

### Mid-Chapter Test 5–B

**1.** $y = -\frac{1}{2}x + 5$   **2.** $y = -\frac{1}{3}x - 1$

**3.** $y = 4x + 2.75$   **4.** $y = -\frac{1}{4}x + \frac{5}{2}$

**5.** $y = 2x + 8$   **6.** $y = 2x - 4$

**7.** $y = -\frac{2}{3}x - 2$   **8.** $y = -5x + 40$

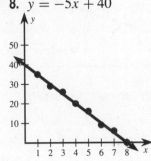

### Chapter Test 5–A

**1.** $y = \frac{1}{3}x - 4$   **2.** $y = -\frac{1}{2}x + 2$

**3.** $y = 3x - 10$   **4.** $y = 2x + 2$

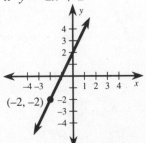

**5.** $y = -2x + 13$   **6.**

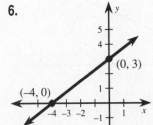

**7.** $y = -3$   **8.** $y = 5x + 10$

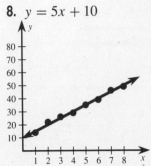

**9.** $3x + 4y = -2$

**10.** $7x + 3y = 1, 7x + 3y = -2$

**11.** $y - 1 = \frac{1}{2}(x + 7)$   **12.** $y = \frac{2}{5}x + \frac{3}{5}$

**13.** $50A + 25B = 1500$   **14.** $D = 180t$

**15.** $y = 250 + 0.02x$   **16.** $V = -3400t + 36,000$

## ■ Chapter Test 5–B

**1.** $y = -\frac{3}{2}x - 5$  **2.** $y = \frac{1}{2}x + 2$

**3.** $y = -4x$  **4.** $y = 4x + 1$

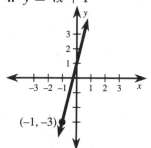

**5.** $y = -2x - 1$  **6.**

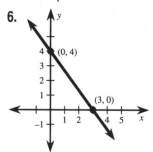

**7.** $x = 7$  **8.** $y = 70 - 8x$

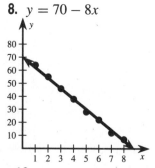

**9.** $2x - 3y = 12$

**10.** $3x - 5y = 2, \ 3x - 5y = -2$

**11.** $y + 7 = \frac{3}{5}(x - 5)$  **12.** $y = \frac{5}{2}x - \frac{3}{2}$

**13.** $30A + 90B = 1800$  **14.** $D = 160t$

**15.** $y = 0.015x + 275$

**16.** $V = -7000t + 75,000$

## ■ Chapter Test 5–C

**1.** $y = -\frac{1}{3}x - 3$  **2.** $y = -\frac{4}{3}x - 4$

**3.** $y = \frac{3}{2}x - \frac{13}{2}$  **4.** $y = \frac{3}{2}x - \frac{3}{2}$

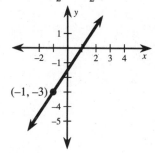

**5.** $y = -\frac{9}{5}x + \frac{58}{5}$  **6.**

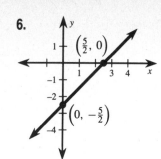

**7.** $x = 0$  **8.** $y = 5x + 10$

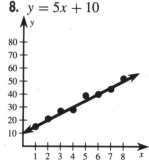

**9.** $3x + 2y = 6$

**10.** $2x - 6y = 3, \ -2x + 6y = 3$

**11.** $y + \frac{3}{2} = -\frac{2}{3}(x - \frac{2}{3})$  **12.** $y = -\frac{2}{3}x - 2$

**13.** $24A + 36B = 2448$

**14.** $D = (t - 2)160 + 90$ or $D = 160t - 230$

**15.** $y = 0.01x + 1500$

**16.** $V = -6500t + 80,000$

## ■ Mid-Chapter Test 6–A

**1.**

**2.** $x \geq -\frac{4}{3}$

**3.** $x > -1$  **4.** $x \geq 3$  **5.** $-10 \leq x < 14$

**6.** $2 \leq x < 5$  **7.** $3 \leq x < 10$

**8.**

**9.** $0.4R + 1.20 \leq 12$ or $R \leq 27$  **10.** $Q \leq 52$

## ■ Mid-Chapter Test 6–B

**1.**

**2.** $x > \frac{7}{8}$

**3.** $x \leq 3$  **4.** $x \geq 4$  **5.** $-15 \leq x < 10$

**6.** $-6 \leq x < -2$  **7.** $2 < x \leq 5$

**8.**

**9.** $0.4R + 1.20 \leq 10$ or $R \leq 22$  **10.** $Q \leq 48$

■ **Chapter Test 6–A**

**1.** $x \le \frac{1}{4}$   **2.**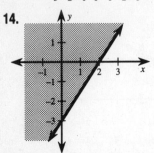

**3.** $x > -2$   **4.** $x < -3$   **5.** $-3 < x \le 1$

**6.** $-\frac{4}{3} < x < -\frac{1}{3}$   **7.** $0 \le x \le 5$

**8.** (number line)   **9.** $13 \le A < 20$

**10.** $3 < x < 11$   **11.** $-1 \le x \le 7$

**12.** (number line)   **13.** Yes

**14.**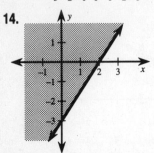

**15.** $415x + 175y \le 100{,}000$
**16. b.** $x > 1, x < -3$   **17.** $2x + 3y \ge 6$
**18.** May 1991 and January 1992

■ **Chapter Test 6–B**

**1.** $x \le -\frac{5}{3}$   **2.** (number line)

**3.** $x \le 1$   **4.** $x \le 4$   **5.** $-2 < x \le -1$

**6.** $-1 < x < 1$   **7.** $3 < x < 7$

**8.** (number line)   **9.** $13 \le A < 18$

**10.** $2 < x < 16$   **11.** $0 \le x \le 4$

**12.** (number line)   **13.** No

**14.**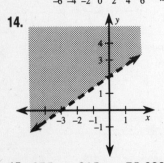

**15.** $375x + 215y \le 75{,}000$
**16. b.** $x > 5, x < -3$   **17.** $4x - y \le -4$
**18.** February, March, and April of 1991

■ **Chapter Test 6–C**

**1.** $x > -\frac{3}{4}$   **2.** (number line)

**3.** $x < -3$ or $x > 1$   **4.** $x < -6$

**5.** $-\frac{1}{2} \le x < \frac{3}{2}$   **6.** $-3 < x \le -1$

**7.** $5 \le x \le 7$   **8.**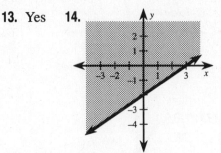

**9.** $157 < W < 163$   **10.** $2 < x < 22$
**11.** $2 < x < 6$   **12.** (number line)

**13.** Yes   **14.**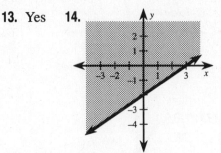

**15.** $27.50x + 45.25y \le 4500$
**16. b.** $-\frac{1}{6} \le x \le \frac{7}{6}$   **17.** $x + y \le -2$
**18.** June, August, and December of 1991

■ **Cumulative Test 1–6**

**1.** $0.57$   **2.** $101.68$   **3.** $\frac{x+7}{11x}$   **4.** $432.04$

**5.** $-121$   **6.** Yes   **7.** $-4B \ge 15$   **8.** $131$

**9.** $\begin{bmatrix} 3 & 4 & 2 \\ 0 & -2 & 11 \end{bmatrix}$   **10.** Yes

**11.** $10 - 7x$   **12.** $N = 3$

**13.** $32.5$ miles per gallon   **14.** $2.29$

**15.** $49.74$ in.$^2$   **16.** $A = \frac{7B}{5-12B}$   **17.** $y = -4$

**18.** \$1.4 billion earnings on approximately \$23 billion revenue in 1986; \$795 million loss on \$29.4 billion revenue in 1991

**19.** Slope: $\frac{4}{7}$; $y$-intercept: $-2$   **20.** $-\frac{3}{4}$

**21.**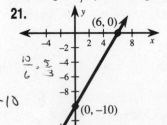

$y = -10$

$\frac{10}{6} = \frac{5}{3}$

$y = +\frac{5}{3}x - 10$

**22.** $-9, -7, -5, -3, -1, 1$

**23.** $y = 7$

**24.** 18 dollars per square yard

**25.** $y = \frac{5}{13}x$

**26.** $y = \frac{3}{2}x - 6$

**27.** $(2, 4)$

**28.** $1, 2, 3, 2, 1$

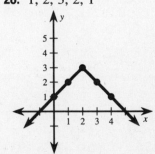

**29.** $y = -\frac{1}{2}x - 1$   **30.** $y = -x + 3$
**31.** $y = -\frac{1}{2}x + \frac{3}{2}$
**32.** $y = 40x - 20$        **33.** $y = 0.05x + 400$
                              **34.** $12x + 10y = 15$
                              **35.** $y + 9 = \frac{1}{5}(x - 4)$

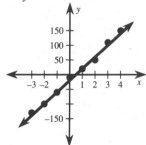

**36.** $V = -17,000t + 180,000$   **37.** $x > -\frac{35}{19}$
**38.** $-4 < x \le 2$   **39.** $x \le -\frac{1}{6}$ or $x \ge \frac{7}{6}$

**40.** Yes   **41.**

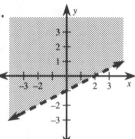

**42.** $y \ge \frac{1}{3}x + 1$
**43.** $39.80x + 49.70y \le 150,000$

## ■ Mid-Chapter Test 7–A

**1.** It is a solution.   **2.** It is not a solution.
**3.** $(1, -1)$          **4.** $(2, -6)$
                          **5.** $(-3, 7)$
                          **6.** $(3, 0)$
                          **7.** $(-2, 3)$

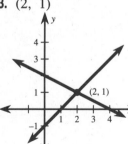

**8.** 4.5 hours at 50 mph; 3.5 hours at 60 mph

## ■ Mid-Chapter Test 7–B

**1.** It is not a solution.   **2.** It is a solution.
**3.** $(2, 1)$              **4.** $(-3, 2)$
                             **5.** $(4, -1)$
                             **6.** $(-4, 7)$
                             **7.** $(0, -2)$

**8.** 3.5 hours at 60 mph; 5.5 hours at 50 mph

## ■ Chapter Test 7–A

**1.** Parallel lines, no solution
**2.** One line only, many solutions
**3.** Intersecting lines, one solution
**4.** $(-1, 2)$          **5.** $(3, -1)$
                          **6.** $(3, -3)$
                          **7.** $\left(\frac{2}{3}, -\frac{1}{2}\right)$
                          **8.** No solution

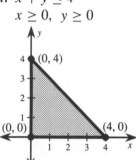

**9.** All points on the line $x + 2y = 4$
**10.** \$2800 at 5%; \$7200 at 7%

**11.** $x + y \le 4$      **12.**
      $x \ge 0, \ y \ge 0$

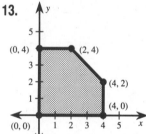

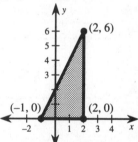

**13.**                    **14.** $C = -38$

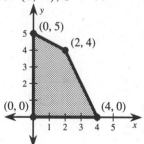

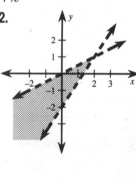

**15.** $(2, 4), C = 44$

## ■ Chapter Test 7–B

**1.** One line, many solutions
**2.** Intersecting lines, one solution
**3.** Parallel lines, no solution

**4.** (2, 1)

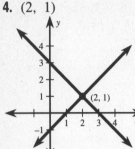

**5.** (4, −3)
**6.** (−5, 6)
**7.** $\left(\frac{1}{2}, -\frac{1}{4}\right)$
**8.** No solution

**9.** All points on the line $3x - y = 2$
**10.** $3500 at 5%; $6500 at 7%

**11.** $x + y \leq 6$
    $x \geq 0, \; y \geq 0$

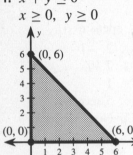

**12.**

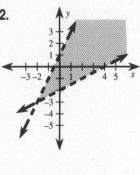

**13.**

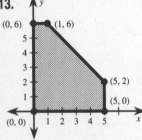

**14.** $C = 6$

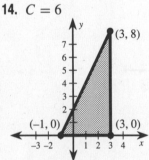

**15.** All points on the line
    $y = -2x + 8, \; C = 32$

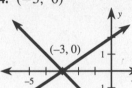

**4.** (−3, 0)

**5.** $\left(-\frac{10}{9}, -\frac{16}{9}\right)$
**6.** (1, −4)
**7.** $\left(-\frac{1}{38}, \frac{4}{19}\right)$
**8.** No solution

**9.** All points on the line $y = 2x - 48$
**10.** $x = 3.75$ lb; $y = 6.25$ lb

**11.** $2x + 3y \leq 18$
    $x \geq 0, \; y \geq 0$

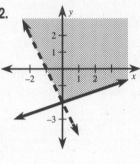

**12.**

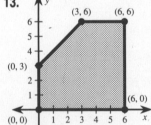

**13.**

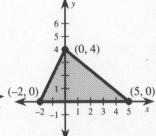

**14.** $C = 30$

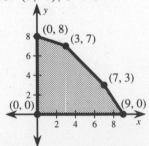

**15.** (3, 7), $C = 54$

■ **Chapter Test 7–C**

1. Intersecting lines, one solution
2. One line, many solutions
3. Parallel lines, no solution

■ **Mid-Chapter Test 8–A**

**1.** $9x^8 y^7$  **2.** $5^3$  **3.** 12  **4.** $\frac{6y^3}{5x^2}$
**5.** 25  **6.** 2  **7.** 1  **8.** 0.625 gram
**9.** $2.1 \times 10^{-1}$ or 0.21  **10.** $5.53 \times 10^{13}$ miles

■ **Mid-Chapter Test 8–B**

**1.** $-8A^8 B^7$  **2.** $5^4$  **3.** 15  **4.** $\frac{-1}{27x^3}$
**5.** 4  **6.** −3  **7.** $\frac{1}{16}$  **8.** 2.5 grams
**9.** $3.6 \times 10^3$ or 3600  **10.** $9.00 \times 10^{13}$ miles

## ■ Chapter Test 8–A

1. $x^{12}$   2. 16   3. 7   4. $\frac{x^2 y}{9}$

5. $-5$   6. $\frac{4}{x^2 y^2}$   7. $\frac{1}{7}$   8. $-\frac{2y^2}{x}$

9. 0.0000000213   10. $5.08 \times 10^7$

11. 350   12. 0.00000734 or $7.34 \times 10^{-6}$

13. $5.99 \times 10^{23}$ protons

14. Approximately 497 seconds or 8.3 minutes

15. $3.795 \times 10^8$ cubic inches   16. $895.42

17. $356.49   18. a. $y = (0.89)^t$   19. 2152

## ■ Chapter Test 8–B

1. $4x^{10}$   2. 64   3. 11   4. $\frac{5A}{B^2}$

5. $-48$   6. $\frac{x^3}{4}$   7. 125   8. $\frac{x^2}{y^3}$

9. 3,940,000,000   10. $4.28 \times 10^{-6}$

11. 2800   12. $3.83 \times 10^{-3}$ or 0.00383

13. $5.99 \times 10^{26}$ protons   14. $6.59 \times 10^{14}$ miles

15. $1.475 \times 10^{-5}$ square inches

16. $983.58   17. $373.63

18. b. $y = (0.79)^t$

19. 1233

## ■ Chapter Test 8–C

1. $-x^9$   2. $-64$   3. 7   4. $\frac{7B^2}{A}$

5. $-\frac{1}{12}$   6. $\frac{x^2 y^2}{3}$   7. $\frac{1}{125}$   8. $\frac{2x}{y^6}$.

9. 0.0000000315   10. $1.93 \times 10^{-11}$

11. 166,000,000   12. $2.86 \times 10^5$ or 286,000

13. $1.10 \times 10^{27}$ electrons

14. Approximately 18.5 light years

15. $2.13 \times 10^4$ cubic feet   16. $938.57

17. $348.28   18. b. $y = (0.94)^t$   19. 1466

## ■ Mid-Chapter Test 9–A

1. $\frac{6}{7}, -\frac{6}{7}$   2. $-14$   3. 17.9

4. 8.29 inches   5. $-8, 8$

6. 5 sec   7. $(-1, -2)$

8. 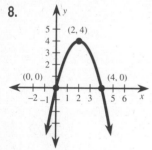   9. 3, $-5$

10. $x = \frac{5}{3}, -2$

## ■ Mid-Chapter Test 9–B

1. $\frac{9}{4}$ and $-\frac{9}{4}$   2. 0.9   3. 12.8

4. 10.51 in.   5. 6, $-6$

6. $\frac{15}{4} = 3.75$ sec   7. $(-2, 3)$

8. 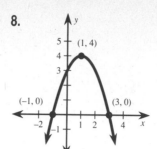   9. $-3, 6$
10. $\frac{3}{4}, -3$

## ■ Chapter Test 9–A

1. 0.5, $-0.5$   2. $-\frac{11}{8}$   3. 5.39

4. 3.24   5. 18, $-18$

6. 3.87, $-3.87$   7. 10.51

8. 3.54 seconds   9. (0, 5), opens down

10. 4.5 meters

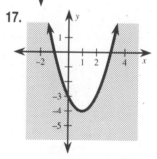

11. 2, $-1$
12. 2.30, $-1.30$
13. 1
14. 5 seconds
15. No
16. Yes

17. 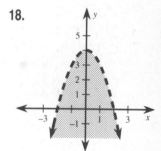   18.

## ■ Chapter Test 9–B

1. 0.8, $-0.8$   2. $-\frac{9}{11}$   3. 6.24

4. $-0.48$   5. 12, $-12$

6. $\pm12.66$   7. 27.5

8. 4.33 sec   9. (0, $-5$), opens up

10. 5.5 meters

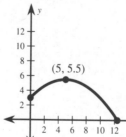

11. 3, $-2$
12. 2.79, $-1.79$
13. 2
14. 6 seconds
15. Yes
16. No

**17.**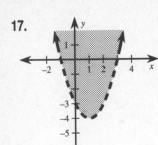

**18.**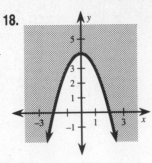

**10.**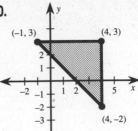

**11.** Maximum 12,
Minimum −45

## ■ Chapter Test 9–C

**1.** 0.09, −0.09  **2.** $-\frac{30}{13}$  **3.** 8.51

**4.** −9.81  **5.** 30, −30

**6.** ±3.85  **7.** 33.8  **8.** 3.98 sec

**9.** Vertex: $\left(\frac{1}{2},\ -\frac{19}{4}\right)$, opens down

**10.** 4 meters

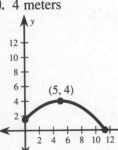

**11.** 1, $-\frac{1}{2}$

**12.** −0.85,
1.18

**13.** None

**14.** 6.25 seconds

**15.** Yes

**16.** No

**17.**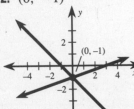

**18.**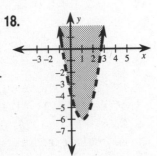

**12.** $3x^{16}$  **13.** −64  **14.** $\frac{y^4}{x^3}$  **15.** $x = 11$

**16.** 1  **17.** $-2a^4$  **18.** 0.0000781

**19.** $7.88 \times 10^{11}$  **20.** 3200

**21.** $3.39 \times 10^{-13}$  **22.** $2.72 \times 10^{26}$ atoms

**23.** 214 seconds or 3 minutes and 34 seconds

**24.** $2.36 \times 10^8$ cubic meters  **25.** $1074.28

**26.** $254.17  **27.** $y = (0.871)^t$  **28.** 2399

**29.** 0.3 and −0.3  **30.** 2.33

**31.** $x = 25,\ x = -25$

**32.** $x = 3.57,\ x = -3.57$  **33.** 46.84

**34.** 5.59 seconds

**35.** Vertex: (0, 10), opens down

**36.**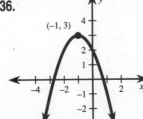

**37.** One

**38.** $x = \frac{3}{2}$,
$x = -1$

**39.** 1.56; −2.56

**40.** Yes

**41.** No

**42.**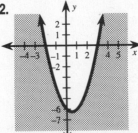

**43.**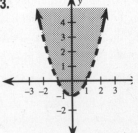

## ■ Cumulative Test 7–9

**1.** Parallel lines, no solution

**2.** (0, −1)

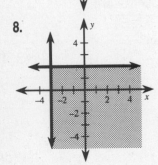

**3.** (4, 1)

**4.** (2, −1)

**5.** $\left(\frac{2}{3},\ 4\right)$

**6.** All points
on the line
$2x - 6y = -1$

**7.** $5500 at 6%,
$9500 at 8%

**8.**

**9.**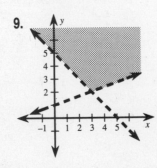

## ■ Mid-Chapter Test 10–A

**1.** $16x^3 + 4x^2 - 7x - 3$  **2.** $2z^3 + z^2 + 5z - 3$

**3.** $3x^2 - 9x$  **4.** $15x^3 - 10x^2$

**5.** $2x^2 - 5x - 3$

**6.** $(x^2 + 14x + 48)$ m²

**7.** $9x^2 - 4$  **8.** $4x^2 - 16x + 16$  **9.** $4x^2 y$

**10.** $2(4x - 7y)(4x + 7y)$

## ■ Mid-Chapter Test 10–B

1. $4x^3 + 5x^2 + x + 3$    2. $2z^3 - z^2 - 3z + 12$
3. $2x^2 - 7x$    4. $32x^3 - 16x^2$
5. $10x^2 + 11x - 6$
6. $(x^2 + 9x + 20)$ m$^2$
7. $4x^2 - 16$    8. $4x^2 - 20x + 25$    9. $5x^2y^3$
10. $3(2x - 1)^2$

## ■ Chapter Test 10–A

1. $7x^2 + 3x + 4$    2. $2x^3 + 2x^2 - 7x - 9$
3. $-11u - 9$    4. $3x^4 - 2x^3 + 4x^2$
5. $3x^2 - 4x - 15$    6. $9x^2 - 12x + 4$
7. $49x^2 - 16$    8. $6A^3B^3$    9. $7z(3z^2 + 4)$
10. $(y + 16)(y - 16)$    11. $(2x + 7y)^2$
12. $3(x + 4)^2$    13. $3x + 2$
14. 12 meters
15. $-3, 7$    16. $-3, \frac{3}{2}$
17. $0, -\frac{2}{5}$    18. 81
19. $-3 + \sqrt{12}, -3 - \sqrt{12}$
20. Length: 80 ft; width: 50 ft

## ■ Chapter Test 10–B

1. $-x^2 - 9x + 15$    2. $2z^3 + 2z^2 + 3z + 13$
3. $-4y - 5$    4. $-6x^4 + 15x^3 + 9x^2$
5. $6x^2 - 7x - 20$    6. $16x^2 - 24x + 9$
7. $64x^2 - 9$    8. $3A^2B^3$    9. $8u^2(3u + 5)$
10. $(z + 9)(z - 9)$    11. $(3x - 5y)^2$
12. $4(m + 5)^2$    13. $5x + 1$
14. 13 meters
15. $-4, -2$    16. $-2, \frac{1}{4}$
17. $0, -\frac{3}{7}$    18. 121
19. $2 + \sqrt{11}, 2 - \sqrt{11}$
20. Length: 70 feet; width: 40 feet

## ■ Chapter Test 10–C

1. $-x^2 + 4x$    2. $2z^3 + 4z^2 + 7z - 4$
3. $A^2 + 13A + 14$    4. $2z^4 + z^3 - 3z^2$
5. $3a^3 - a^2 + 6a - 2$    6. $x^4 - 8x^2 + 16$
7. $25z^4 - 9$    8. $8A^8y^6$    9. $6u^4v^4(3v + 5u)$
10. $(9z + 11)(9z - 11)$    11. $(4x^2 + 5y^2)^2$
12. $5m^2(m - 7)^2$    13. $x^2 + 1$
14. 11.5 meters
15. $\frac{3}{2}, -\frac{2}{3}$    16. $-\frac{6}{5}, \frac{5}{6}$
17. $0, \frac{3}{7}$    18. $\frac{225}{4} = 56.25$
19. $-\frac{5}{2} + \frac{\sqrt{17}}{2}, \frac{-5}{2} - \frac{\sqrt{17}}{2}$
20. Length: 90 feet; width: 50 feet

## ■ Mid-Chapter Test 11–A

1. $\frac{10}{7}$    2. $-2, 4$
3. 105 meters    4. 13.8%    5. 1400
6. $y = 4x$    7. $PV = 1440$
8. 0.15    9. 0    10. $\frac{1}{3}$

## ■ Mid-Chapter Test 11–B

1. 11    2. $-2, 3$
3. 204 pounds    4. 15.8%    5. 1240
6. $y = \frac{3}{4}x$    7. $PV = 21$
8. 0.125    9. 1    10. $\frac{2}{5}$

## ■ Chapter Test 11–A

1. $\frac{31}{2}$    2. $5, -3$
3. 32.4 miles    4. 23.8%    5. 250
6. $W = 4l$    7. $xy = 125$
8. $\frac{1}{2}$    9. 0.01    10. 0.75
11. All real numbers except 0 and 6
12. $\frac{x-3}{x}$    13. $\frac{13}{8x^2}$    14. $\frac{1}{4}$
15. $\frac{12x^2(x+1)}{11}$    16. $6N^2 + 5N - 1$
17. Quotient: $x^2 + 2x + 4$; Remainder: $-10$
18. $3x + 4 + \frac{15}{x-2}$    19. $4, -6$
20. 50,000 doz

## ■ Chapter Test 11–B

1. 10    2. $-2, 7$
3. 475 yards    4. 8.9%    5. 2500
6. $V = 25h$    7. $RS = 270$
8. 0.1    9. 0.1    10. 0.2
11. All real numbers except 0 and $-3$
12. $\frac{x}{x-4}$    13. $\frac{10}{3}x$    14. $\frac{1}{2(x+4)}$
15. $\frac{10}{9}y(y - 2)$    16. $3y^3 - 4y^2 + 5y$
17. Quotient: $x + 6$; Remainder: 10
18. $4x - 11 + \frac{13}{x+1}$    19. $-6, 2$
20. 40,000 doz

## ■ Chapter Test 11–C

1. $\frac{5}{7}$    2. $2 + \sqrt{10}, 2 - \sqrt{10}$
3. 51.3 bushels    4. 3.5%    5. 7280
6. $W = 53l$    7. $PQ = 2017.2$
8. $\frac{2}{3}$    9. 0.01    10. 0.72
11. All real numbers except $-4$ and 1
12. $\frac{x+2}{x-2}$    13. $\frac{3}{4x^5}$    14. $\frac{2}{x-1}$
15. $\frac{4(x+2)}{3x^2(x-2)}$    16. $6x + 8 - \frac{2}{x}$
17. Quotient: $x^2 + 2x + 4$; Remainder: 8
18. $4x^2 + 5x + 1 + \frac{2}{2x-1}$    19. $-2$
20. 40,000 doz

## ■ Mid-Chapter Test 12–A

**1.** It does. Domain: {0, 1, 2, 3}   **2.** No
**3.** 4   **4.** No   **8.** 3, maximum
**5.** $f(x) = \frac{1}{2}x + \frac{7}{2}$
**6.** Shift graph of $f$
1 unit up to
obtain graph of $g$.
**7.** Vertex: $(-2, -7)$;
lowest point

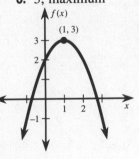

## ■ Mid-Chapter Test 12–B

**1.** It does. Domain: {$a, b, c, d$}
**2.** No   **3.** 5   **4.** Yes
**5.** $f(x) = -\frac{2}{5}x + \frac{21}{5}$
**6.** Reflect graph of $f$
in $x$-axis to
obtain graph of $g$.
**7.** Vertex: $(3, 4)$;
highest point   **8.** $-2$, minimum

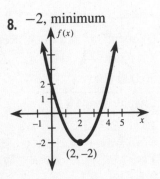

## ■ Chapter Test 12–A

**1.** No
**2.** It does. Domain: {0, 1, 2, 3, 4}
**3.** $-1$   **4.** $-\frac{8}{5}$   **5.** $f(x) = 10x - 14$
**6.**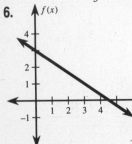
**7.** Reflect graph of $f$
in $x$-axis to
obtain graph of $g$.
**8.** Shift graph of $f$
1 unit to right to
obtain graph of $g$.
**9.** Shift graph of $f$ 5 units up to obtain graph of $g$.
**10.**   **11.**

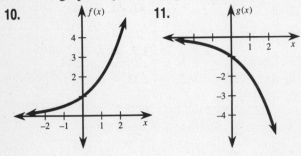

**12.** Vertex: $(-3, 7)$; highest point
**13.** $f(x) = (x + 2)^2 - 4$   **14.** Center: (4, 5)
Asymptotes:
$x = 4$,  $y = 5$

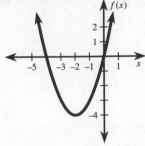

**15.** $f(x) = \frac{x+5}{2x+2}$   **16.** $f(x) = \frac{-1}{x+1} + 4$

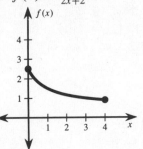

**17.** 19
**18.**

| Stem-and-Leaf Plot | | Ordered data |
|---|---|---|
| 9 | 7 8 | 98, 97 |
| 8 | 2 8 | 88, 82 |
| 7 | 5 5 1 2 1 | 75, 75, 72, 71, 71 |
| 6 | 5 3 7 5 | 67, 65, 65, 63 |
| 5 | 1 9 4 | 59, 54, 51 |
| 4 | 4 9 | 49, 44 |
| 3 | 8 7 4 | 38, 37, 34 |
| 2 | 4 7 9 | 29, 27, 24 |
| 1 | 9 3 4 4 | 19, 14, 14, 13 |

**19.** $8\frac{1}{3}$   **20.** Median: 8; mode: 8

## ■ Chapter Test 12–B

**1.** No
**2.** It does. Domain: {$a, b, c, d$}
**3.** 1   **4.** $\frac{2}{3}$   **5.** $f(x) = \frac{5}{3}x - 4$
**6.**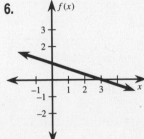
**7.** Shift graph of $f$
2 units to right to
obtain graph of $g$.
**8.** Shift graph of $f$
4 units down to
obtain graph of $g$.
**9.** Reflect graph of $f$
in $x$-axis to
obtain graph of $g$.

**10.**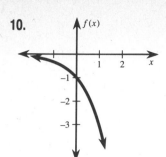

**11.**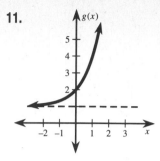

**6.**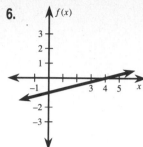

**7.** Shift $f$ up $\frac{1}{2}$ unit.

**8.** Reflect $f$ in the $x$-axis.

**9.** Shift $f$ left 3 units.

**12.** $(2, -7)$; lowest point

**13.** $f(x) = (x - 3)^2 + 4$

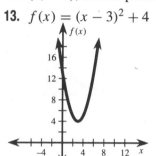

**14.** Center: $(-3, -4)$
Asymptotes:
$x = -3, y = -4$

**10.**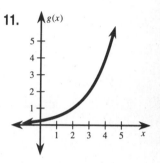

**11.** 

**12.** $\left(\frac{1}{2}, \frac{7}{4}\right)$, highest point

**13.** $f(x) = -(x - 1)^2 + 3$

**14.** Center: $(3, -6)$
Asymptotes:
$x = 3, y = -6$

**15.** $f(x) = \frac{x+6}{2x+3}$

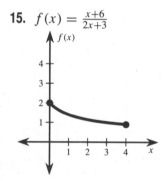

**16.**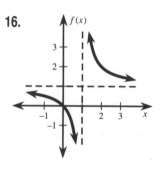

**15.** $f(x) = \frac{x+4}{2x+3}$

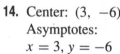

**16.**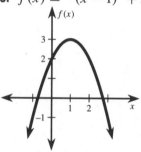

**17.** 42

**18.**

| Stem-and-Leaf Plot | | Ordered data |
|---|---|---|
| 9 | 7 4 | 97, 94 |
| 8 | 1 7 | 87, 81 |
| 7 | 8 7 | 78, 77 |
| 6 | 4 5 5 0 7 | 67, 65, 65, 64, 60 |
| 5 | 5 9 1 6 | 59, 56, 55, 51 |
| 4 | 9 1 4 7 3 0 | 49, 47, 44, 43, 41, 40 |
| 3 | 3 3 | 33, 33 |
| 2 | 7 4 5 8 1 | 28, 27, 25, 24, 21 |

**19.** $6\frac{2}{3}$   **20.** Median: 6.5; mode: 5 and 8

■ **Chapter Test 12–C**

**1.** Yes   **2.** It does not

**3.** 0   **4.** $-\frac{1}{2}$   **5.** $f(x) = \frac{1}{3}x - \frac{8}{3}$

**17.** 37.5

**18.**

| Stem-and-Leaf Plot | | Ordered data |
|---|---|---|
| 2 | 8 9 5 2 0 | 20, 22, 25, 28, 29 |
| 3 | 7 3 5 2 | 32, 33, 35, 37 |
| 4 | 4 7 1 4 | 41, 44, 44, 47 |
| 5 | 2 2 9 9 | 52, 52, 59, 59 |
| 6 | 7 4 9 3 3 | 63, 63, 64, 67, 69 |
| 7 | 6 1 5 1 0 | 70, 71, 71, 75, 76 |
| 8 | 0 | 80 |

**19.** $6\frac{5}{6}$   **20.** Median: 6.5; mode: 4

## ■ Cumulative Test 7–12

**1.** Parallel lines; no solution    **2.** $(3, -1)$

**3.** All points on the line $2x - 5y = 6$

**4.** $7500 at 6\%; $12,500 at 7\%

**5.**

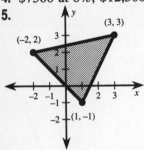

**6.** 14    **7.** $\frac{x^2}{9}$    **8.** $\frac{x^5}{y^8}$    **9.** 3

**10.** $\frac{a^2}{2b}$    **11.** $7.94 \times 10^{14}$

**12.** 6300    **13.** $3.92 \times 10^{20}$

**14.** $5.05 \times 10^9$ miles

**15.** $1096.82    **16.** $558.39

**17.** b.  $y = (0.67)^t$

**18.** $0.9, -0.9$    **19.** 3.08

**20.** $3.76, -3.76$

**21.**

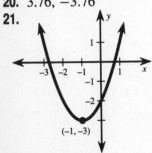

**22.** $-3.45, 1.45$

**23.**

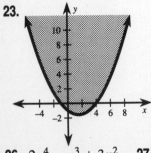

**24.** $-x - 20$
**25.** $6x^2 - x - 15$

**26.** $2x^4 - x^3 + 3x^2$    **27.** $15A^3B^2$

**28.** $(2y - 7)(2y + 7)$    **29.** $2(x - 4y)^2$

**30.** $\frac{1}{2}, -\frac{3}{2}$    **31.** $0, \frac{2}{7}$

**32.** Width: 40 feet; length: 65 feet

**33.** $-4$    **34.** 24%

**35.** 160    **36.** $xy = 312$    **37.** $\frac{1}{3}$    **38.** $\frac{5}{9}$

**39.** All real numbers except 0 and $-4$

**40.** $\frac{9xy}{4}$    **41.** $5A - 4 - \frac{3}{A}$

**42.** It is. Domain: $\{-2, 0, 2, 4\}$    **43.** 11

**44.** $f(x) = \frac{1}{2}x - 3$

**45.**

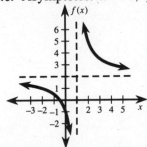

**46.** Asymptotes: $x = 1, \ y = 2$

**47.** Mean: 27, median: 28, mode: 32

## ■ Mid-Chapter Test 13–A

**1.** $3\sqrt{5}$    **2.** Yes    **3.** $(\frac{7}{2}, -2)$

**4.** $\frac{1}{8}\sqrt{26}$    **5.** $15\sqrt{2}$    **6.** $11\sqrt{3}$

**7.** 6    **8.** $2\sqrt{10}$

## ■ Mid-Chapter Test 13–B

**1.** $2\sqrt{5}$    **2.** Yes    **3.** $(6, \frac{1}{2})$

**4.** $\frac{\sqrt{6}}{12}$    **5.** $14\sqrt{3}$    **6.** $3\sqrt{2}$

**7.** 7    **8.** $2\sqrt{15}$

## ■ Chapter Test 13–A

**1.** $\sqrt{61} \approx 7.81$    **2.** Yes    **3.** $(\frac{1}{2}, \frac{1}{2})$

**4.** $\frac{2}{9}\sqrt{15}$    **5.** $2\sqrt{3} + 3\sqrt{2}$    **6.** $\sqrt{5}$

**7.** $4\sqrt{3} + 6\sqrt{2} \approx 15.41$

**8.** $3 + 3\sqrt{3}$    **9.** 9

**10.** No solution    **11.** $2\sqrt{21} \approx 9.17$

**12.** $\tan A = \frac{7}{4}, \tan B = \frac{4}{7}$

**13.** 0.804    **14.** 8.60    **15.** $\frac{27}{2} = 13.5$

**16.** 5.3 meters

**17.** Commutative axiom of addition

**18.** $a = 3, \ b = 4, \ (3 + 4)^2 \neq 3^2 + 4^2$

(Answers vary.)

## ■ Chapter Test 13–B

**1.** $\sqrt{97} \approx 9.85$    **2.** Yes    **3.** $(6, \frac{1}{2})$

**4.** $\frac{3}{4}\sqrt{6}$    **5.** $4 + 2\sqrt{6}$    **6.** $\frac{\sqrt{2}}{3}$

**7.** $10\sqrt{6} \approx 24.49$

**8.** $3 - 3\sqrt{3}$    **9.** 10

**10.** No solution    **11.** $4\sqrt{5} \approx 8.94$

**12.** $\tan A = \frac{12}{5}$, $\tan B = \frac{5}{12}$

**13.** 0.29    **14.** 15.26    **15.** 23 ft

**16.** $\frac{77}{5} = 15.4$

**17.** Commutative axiom of multiplication

**18.** $a = 5$, $b = 3$, $(5 - 3)^2 \neq 5^2 - 3^2$

(Answers vary.)

■ **Chapter Test 13–C**

**1.** $\frac{\sqrt{29}}{4} \approx 1.35$    **2.** No    **3.** $\left(-\frac{1}{2}, \frac{1}{2}\right)$

**4.** $\frac{7}{9}\sqrt{6}$    **5.** $5\sqrt{3} - 3\sqrt{5}$    **6.** $\frac{3}{2}$

**7.** $12(\sqrt{6} + 1) \approx 41.39$

**8.** $2 - 4\sqrt{2}$    **9.** No solution

**10.** 1, 2    **11.** $\sqrt{435} \approx 20.86$

**12.** $\tan A = \frac{7}{12}$, $\tan B = \frac{12}{7}$

**13.** 1.905    **14.** $c \approx 15.62$, $A \approx 40°$

**15.** $B = 69°$, $b \approx 13.0$

**16.** $b = 20$, $c \approx 21.5$

**17.** Associative axiom of addition

**18.** Not true for $a = 2$, $b = 3$, $c = -1$

$2(-1) \not< 3(-1)$

(Answers vary.)

# Answers to Practice for College Entrance Tests

## Chapter 1, Form A
1. B  2. E  3. E  4. D  5. B
6. A  7. B  8. E  9. A  10. C

## Chapter 1, Form B
1. A  2. B  3. C  4. A  5. C
6. D  7. D  8. B  9. C  10. A

## Chapter 2, Form A
1. D  2. B  3. D  4. B  5. C
6. C  7. C  8. D  9. C

## Chapter 2, Form B
1. 9  2. 11  3. 1.14  4. 7.56
5. 195  6. 24  7. 64  8. 10
9. 75  10. 63  11. $\frac{1}{10}$  12. 36

## Chapter 3, Form A
1. E  2. E  3. C  4. B  5. C
6. C  7. E  8. E  9. D  10. C

## Chapter 3, Form B
1. C  2. A  3. B  4. B  5. C
6. D  7. B  8. A  9. A  10. C

## Chapter 4, Form A
1. E  2. A  3. B  4. C  5. D
6. A

## Chapter 4, Form B
1. $\frac{4}{3}$  2. 2  3. 1.6  4. 1
5. 1  6. 2
7. Any value including and between 2 and 6
8. 500  9. 3 or 11  10. 1 or 9

## Chapter 5, Form A
1. C  2. D  3. E  4. E  5. B
6. D

## Chapter 5, Form B
1. B  2. A  3. B  4. C  5. A
6. D

## Chapter 6, Form A
1. E  2. C  3. B  4. C  5. A
6. E  7. A

## Chapter 6, Form B
1. Any value greater than 1
2. Any value greater than or equal to 10
3. $\frac{2}{3}$ or 2
4. Any value less than or equal to 10
5. $\frac{1}{15}$
6. Any value between and including 48 and 60
7. 6  8. $\frac{1}{2}$ or 0.5  9. 1300  10. 850

## Chapter 7, Form A
1. A  2. B  3. D  4. E  5. B
6. A  7. E  8. C

## Chapter 7, Form B
1. B  2. C  3. A  4. A  5. B
6. A  7. A  8. D  9. B

## Chapter 8, Form A
1. E  2. C  3. B  4. C  5. E
6. E  7. C  8. B  9. E  10. C

## Chapter 8, Form B
1. 4  2. 8  3. 4  4. 7  5. 6
6. 5.20  7. 64  8. 0.04  9. 8
10. 12.5 or $\frac{25}{2}$  11. 7  12. 0

## Chapter 9, Form A
1. D  2. E  3. E  4. B  5. D
6. A  7. B  8. A  9. C

## Chapter 9, Form B
1. C  2. D  3. B  4. A  5. D
6. B  7. A  8. C  9. A

## Chapter 10, Form A
1. D  2. B  3. C  4. A  5. C
6. E

## Chapter 10, Form B
1. 3  2. 9  3. 7  4. 4
5. 4  6. 40  7. 14  8. 3

## Chapter 11, Form A
1. E  2. D  3. A  4. E  5. D
6. B  7. E  8. A  9. A

## Chapter 11, Form B
1. B  2. A  3. C  4. D  5. D
6. B  7. D  8. C  9. A

## Chapter 12, Form A

**1.** E    **2.** C    **3.** C    **4.** E

## Chapter 12, Form B

**1.** Any value between, but not including, 1 and 3

**2.** 9    **3.** 4 or 6    **4.** 5

**5.** $\frac{5}{4}$ or 1.25    **6.** 3

**7.** 1    **8.** 2 or 4    **9.** $\frac{1}{3}$

**10.** $\frac{3}{2}$ or 1.5

## Chapter 13, Form A

**1.** C    **2.** C    **3.** A    **4.** C    **5.** B

**6.** B    **7.** E

## Chapter 13, Form B

**1.** A    **2.** D    **3.** C    **4.** A    **5.** B

**6.** A    **7.** C    **8.** B